# SKILLS

# DESIGN AND TECHNOLOGY

Jenny Ridgwell with Louise Davies

HEINEMANN
EDUCATIONAL

Heinemann Educational,
a division of **Heinemann Educational Books Ltd**,
Halley Court, Jordan Hill, Oxford OX2 8EJ

OXFORD LONDON EDINBURGH MADRID
ATHENS BOLOGNA PARIS MELBOURNE
SYDNEY AUCKLAND SINGAPORE TOKYO
IBADAN NAIROBI HARARE GABORONE
PORTSMOUTH NH (USA)

© Jenny Ridgwell with Louise Davies 1990

First published 1990
91 92 93 94 95 12 11 10 9 8 7 6 5 4 3

**British Library Cataloguing in Publication Data**
Ridgwell, Jenny
 Skills in design and technology.
 1. Design & technology.
 I. Title  II. Davies, Louise
 600

ISBN 0 435 42003 8

Produced by Gecko Limited, Bicester, Oxon

Printed and bound in Spain by Mateu Cromo

The Design and technology checklist on pp. 92–93 may be
freely photocopied for classroom use in the purchasing
institution.

## Acknowledgements

Thanks are due to the following people for permission to
reproduce copyright material: Association of Market Survey
Organisations Ltd for the text and illustration on p. 20; Peter
Bazalgette for 'The chilling facts of safe home cooking' on
p. 40, which appeared in the *Sunday Times*, 22 January
1988; Birds Eye Wall's for Wall's Pocket Money Monitor on
p. 43 and Wall's Report on p. 42; British Blind Sport for the
use of their address on p. 39; British Telecommunications
PLC for the BT logo on p. 94, the telephone charges
information on p. 28, and the *Yellow Pages* extract on p. 29;
Duckwork and Company Limited for Heath Robinson
illustrations on p. 78; EAG Scientific Report for Charts A and
B on p. 41; Kelda Free of the United World College of South
East Asia in Singapore for her design on p. 74; Friends for
the Young Deaf for the use of their address p. 39; Halifax
Building Society for Halifax *Quest* Club Magazine
Questionnaire 1989 on p. 45; ILECC for the SURVEY
Computer Program on p. 44; ITV Oracle for the extract
from Oracle on p. 38; The Jacob's Bakery Limited for
*Nabisco View of a Biscuit Market* on p. 42; Mars
Confectionery, a Division of Mars UK Limited for the use of
the 'Tracker' labels on p. 86; Ministry of Agriculture,
Fisheries and Food for the cover of *Food sense* on p. 41; E.
Pitt for the illustrations on pp. 56–57; Tefal UK Limited for
'Behind the scenes a kettle is born' pp. 12–13; Tidy Britain
Group for the illustration of Tidy Man on p. 14; Trustees of
the Science Museum, Science Museum Library for 'A clock
that makes tea' on p. 78; Wandsworth Borough Council for
the poster of Bobby the Bottle and Friends on p. 14; *Which?*
for 'Your views on Green products' pp. 46–47 and the orange
juice survey on pp. 72–73.

Thanks are also due for the following for permission to
reproduce photographs: Barnaby's Picture Library, p. 56;
J. Allan Cash Ltd, p. 20; The Design Council, all on pp. 90–
91, p. 14; Sally and Richard Greenhill, p. 48; Robert Harding
Picture Library, p. 52, p. 53; Stephen Oliver, p. 62; Georgina
Ravenscroft, pp. 76–77; Chris Ridgers, p. 28, p. 34,
pp. 48–49; The Tea Council Ltd, p. 68; Tefal UK Ltd,
pp. 12–13; Topham Picture Source, p. 78; *Which*/Jim
Forrest, p. 12. All other photographs supplied by Louise
Davies and Jenny Ridgwell.

Cover illustration by Pat Thorne

# Contents

Identifying the need or opportunity for design

Researching and finding things out

Generating a design proposal

## Planning and making

## Presenting your ideas

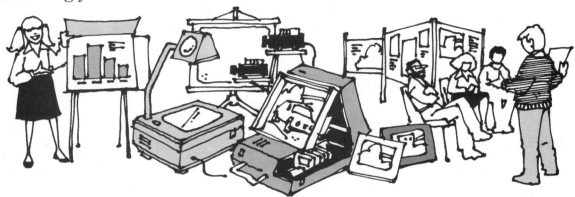

## Evaluating

### *Discuss*

Think of a design idea. Discuss how you could work through the design process to develop and make your idea.

5

# What is design and technology?

Design and technology is about finding solutions to meet people's needs. How do these designs meet people's needs?

? Recycling area

School dinners

? Chinese festival design

How do these designs meet people's needs?

? Playgrounds

? People in wheelchairs

Disc jockey at a radio station

Meeting needs

Designs may fall into groups.
**Artefacts** – objects or things such as a packed lunch or a wheelchair ramp
**Systems** – the way things work – a playgroup game
**Environments** – what is all around us, our surroundings – a cleaner environment by recycling

Sometimes a design can belong to two or even three groups.

School meals are artefacts, but they are part of a system – your school lunch service – and you eat them in the dining room – an environment.

Artefacts and systems

## Discuss

Use the pictures on these pages or your own ideas of designs around you. Talk about how designs meet our needs. Record your findings.

Try to sort out the designs into artefacts, systems and environments – or maybe they belong to more than one group.

## Contexts

All designs fit into a **context** – the situation in which design and technology activity takes place. Contexts may be any of these.

> home   school   recreation   community
> business and industry

*Recycling* could fit into the context of *community* or *business*. If you redesigned your bedroom then this could be in the context of *home*.

## Discuss

What contexts might the designs illustrated on this page fit into? Remember, they may belong to several contexts.

Where do they fit?

# People's needs

A successful design meets people's needs. They could need a cleaner environment, a safe place to work or just warm clothes – all three involve designs.

What are people's needs? Let's start with *you*!

## My needs

My needs

Imagine that you were one of these teenagers. How could you develop a **design proposal** to meet these needs?

My ideas

## Discuss

On your own or in a group, make a list of *your own* needs. Any ideas are welcome! Compare your notes with others. Can you think of more?

**Brainstorm** your group (see page 14). Think of ways to develop a design proposal for one of your needs. Use a **spider diagram** to help.

## Other people's needs

People may have different needs to you.

Different needs

## *Discuss*

In a group, choose one of the people shown above or think of someone you know. Brainstorm to think about their needs, then come up with a design proposal for ways you could help or make a list of problems you could investigate. You may get ideas from the example below.

Ways to help

## Group needs

People belong to many different groups. Each group has its own needs.

## *Discuss*

Think of your own group or use the pictures below. What are the needs of these groups? Brainstorm to get ideas to design or investigate for the needs of a group.

Group needs

# Cleaning up — a design project

Cleaning up

## Discuss

What can *you* do about rubbish?
**Brainstorm** your group to get ideas (see page 14).

## Plan

What can you do about the rubbish problem? Choose an idea then *plan* your course of action.

- Organize your *group* carefully — you need to be clear about your *aims* before you start researching.
- Keep a *record* of your work. This could be written notes, photos, recordings.

Old newspaper is collected for recycling — it raises £17 000 a year for charity

Brainstorming for ideas

## Research

### Ideas

You could make some *telephone calls* to find out what is happening in your area. Recycling activities change quickly so using the telephone will give you up-to-date information.

*Write* letters to find out what happens to waste around the country.

*Visit* local bottle banks and **observe** how they are used. Take some *pictures* to show the rubbish problem in your area.

*Interview* to find out what people think about the rubbish problem and what is needed to improve matters.

### Design and make

Decide what action your group will take about the rubbish problem.

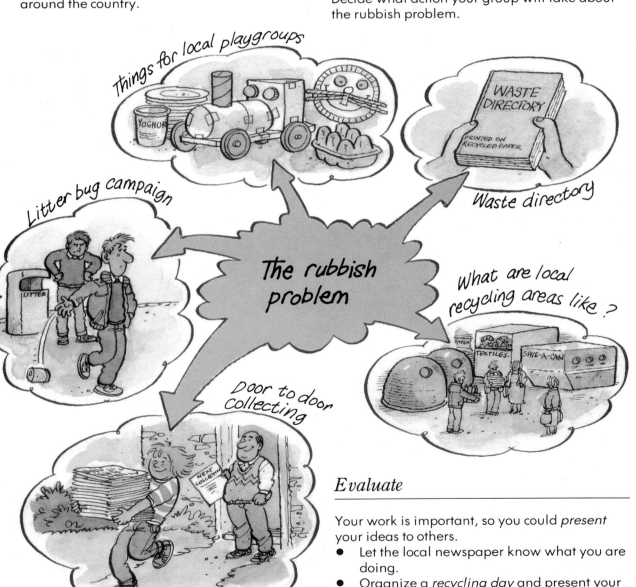

Things for local playgroups

Waste directory

Litter bug campaign

The rubbish problem

What are local recycling areas like?

Door to door collecting

### Evaluate

Your work is important, so you could *present* your ideas to others.
- Let the local newspaper know what you are doing.
- Organize a *recycling day* and present your ideas to an audience.
- Invite an expert from your local council to comment.

These people can **evaluate** your work too.

Talking rubbish

In real life, how is a new product designed?

Tefal asked a team of designers to create a new cordless jug kettle. These are the stages which the designers and manufacturers went through to create a new design.

### Stage 1  Discussing
Tefal wanted to make the first cordless kettle. First the company described the kind of new product they wanted to the designers. This is called *the briefing*.

### Stage 2  Researching
Then the designers **brainstormed** to get ideas for their research.

> Let's look at existing products, take them apart and see how they are made.

> Then we can discover their strengths and weaknesses and sort out design problems

Identifying design problems

### Stage 3  Planning the design
The design team came up with four or five rough **sketches**. Then they made polystyrene and wood **models** and a **prototype** . . .

Models

. . . and an **exploded view**.

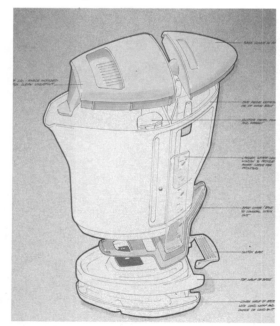

An exploded view

### Stage 4  Presenting design ideas for evaluation
These ideas were presented to the company to get their views. The chosen design was presented as a detailed drawing. The design team discussed details such as colour choices, graphics – letters, numbers and decorations – with the company.

## Stage 5  Designing and making

An accurate non-working model was built. Final engineering drawings were completed.

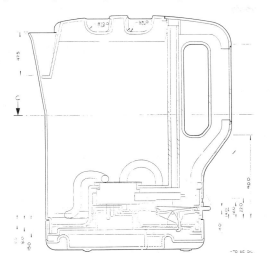

An engineering drawing

## Stage 6  Testing it out

Work started to make the machinery for large-scale production. Costs and production machinery were checked. A *test run* of about 250 kettles was carried out. Consumers were asked for their views.

Problems were sorted out and *quality control* was checked before full scale production.

Making kettles in a factory

## Stage 7  Evaluating

The first Freeline cordless kettle was very successful but by the time the kettle had reached the shops, plans were already being made for new designs.

# Changes in design

- The lid was moulded in one piece – it was cheaper to make and fitted better.
- The pilot light was removed and the graphics on the water level indicator used one colour instead of two to cut costs.

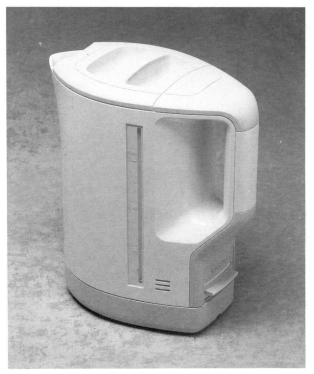

The new-look Freeline

In 1989 the Freeline changed again.
- A fail-safe device was added to prevent overheating.
- The shape was changed to make the kettle softer and rounder.

## *Discuss and record*

Make a list of the stages the design team went through to design the new cordless kettle.
- How did they get ideas?
- How did they describe their design?
- What changes did they make to adapt their design?
- What constraints did they face with this design?
- What do you think about the designs of the Freeline cordless kettle?

13

# Getting started with designing

## Brainstorming

One way of getting started on your project is to **brainstorm** your group to get *ideas*.

- Any number of people can be involved.
- Any ideas are worth thinking about.
- Allow a set time – say 15 minutes – to come up with lots of ideas.
- Write down everyone's ideas on a **spider diagram**.

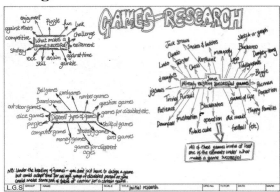

Brainstorming session

## Sorting out ideas

From the brainstorming session, each idea can be looked at more carefully. Ideas need to be sorted into order of importance. This is called **prioritizing**.

Prioritizing

## No ideas?

Sometimes you can be stumped for ideas. *Triggers* such as newspaper cuttings, posters, photos or videos about the area you are researching can spark off new plans.

Bobby the Bottle poster reproduced by kind permission of Wandsworth Borough Council

Tidy Britain Group poster

## Igloo sites for rubbish

Igloos are set to spring up all over Merton. But don't panic – they are not to house an Eskimo invasion, but to collect rubbish for recycling.

Merton Council plans to site small igloo-shaped bins all over the borough in car parks and streets.

The idea is that residents deposit their recyclable rubbish at handy local points.

Sites may include the Savacentre in Colliers Wood, Mitcham Fair Green, Morden Library and the Hartfield Road car park.

A report to councillors said: 'It is essential that the council should have a proper strategy, geared to an energetic and vigorous recycling campaign. Every tonne of refuse which is recycled saves the ratepayer approximately £20 because it does not have to be taken away to a disposal site.'

Recycling — report from *Wimbledon Guardian*

## *Discuss*

Work in a group and use the posters and newspaper cutting as triggers to give you ideas for an investigation into recycling waste in your area. Draw a spider diagram to show your results.

## Working together

You can get lots of ideas and help when working in a group. Most people work in groups to get things done.

## *Discuss*

In a group, think of as many different real life groups as you can.
- Why is it useful for these people to be in a group?
- Does each group need a leader?
- How is each group run – what does it do?
- Discuss the value of working with others.

## Organizing a group

In your group, come up with some tips for organizing group work.
Here are some thoughts to start you off.
- Listen to everyone's point of view.
- Change the *size* of the group to see which works best.

Working in groups

## *Evaluate*

Look at the list of tasks below.
- getting ideas
- interviewing someone
- making notes from books
- visiting a library
- listening to a radio programme
- shopping

Is it better to work in a group, in a pair or alone to complete these tasks?

Copy the chart below and complete it for all the tasks above giving short reasons for your choice.

| Task | It is better to work | | | Why? |
| | in a group | in a pair | alone | |
|---|---|---|---|---|
| listening to the radio | | | ✓ | because I can concentrate better alone |

15

# Questionnaires

When you want to find out what people think, you ask them questions. A **questionnaire** is just one way of organizing this information by using a list of questions.

### Designing a questionnaire.
- What is your *aim*? What do you need to find out about? Write a *title* for your questionnaire to remind yourself.
- Write out the questions in rough first, then test them out on others. You may need to make changes if they don't make sense.

### Writing questions.
- Ask easy questions first, otherwise you put people off!
- Try asking questions with a 'yes' or 'no' answer or with just two answer choices.
- Try multiple choice questions where there are several answers to choose from.

1. Do you have school lunches?
   yes ☐  no ☐
2. What do you eat for lunch?
   school lunch ☐  packed lunch ☐
   visit cafe/chip shop ☐  other ☐

These are *closed* questions – questions with straightforward answers. The answers are **facts**.
- Include a question to find out **opinions** – what people think. These are called *open-ended* questions.
- *Check* that your questionnaire meets your *aim* – what you need to find out.
- Plan it out.
- Leave spaces for the answers.
- Use boxes to tick off replies.

You can write out the questionnaire by hand, type it or use a word-processing program on a computer.

Here are some hints for organizing and filling in questionnaires.
- Get organized before you start. You may need several copies of your questionnaire, a clipboard or folder, pen or pencil.
- Get permission to leave lessons for out-of-school visits.
- If people are busy, leave them the questionnaire and arrange to collect it later.
- Be polite when you ask people questions.
- As soon as you have finished, sort out your results.

## Getting results

Think about who will fill in the answers to your questionnaire – you or the people themselves. How will you keep a record of the replies – by writing or recording what they say?

## *Discuss*

Look at the *carrier bag survey* opposite. What do you think is the *aim* of the questionnaire – what information are they seeking?
Decide which of the questions are finding out
- facts – closed questions
- opinions – open questions.

How do you think the results of this survey could be used?

## *Design and make*

Questionnaires are not easy to design.
Plan and test out a short questionnaire. Work on your own, in pairs or in a group. Use the ideas from these pages to help.
*Test* out your questionnaire on a friend.
Ask for their comments on how you could improve your questionnaire.
Rewrite your questions if necessary.

# CARRIER BAG SURVEY

Name of Respondent _____ Date _____

Sex: Male ☐ Female ☐

Age: Under 16 ☐ 16–34 ☐

35–64 ☐ 65+ ☐

(Please tick appropriate boxes)

This is your first/second re-usable carrier bag (code ____)

Please use the carrier bag at least once with a full load of shopping etc. before answering the following questions.

Thinking only about the HANDLE of the carrier bag, how does it feel in your hand when the bag is fully loaded? Does the HANDLE FEEL:

Very comfortable ☐
Fairly comfortable ☐ (Tick
Neither comfortable nor uncomfortable ☐ appropriate
Fairly uncomfortable ☐ box)
Very uncomfortable ☐

And now thinking about the OVERALL STRENGTH of the carrier bag, would you say the bag is:

Very strong ☐
Fairly strong ☐ (Tick
Neither strong nor weak ☐ appropriate
Fairly weak ☐ box)
Very weak ☐

Taking everything into consideration, how SATISFACTORY did you find this re-usable carrier bag which you might have purchased in the normal way. Was the bag:

Very satisfactory ☐ (Tick
Fairly satisfactory ☐ appropriate
Neither satisfactory nor unsatisfactory ☐ box)
Fairly unsatisfactory ☐ } (please
Very unsatisfactory ☐ answer below)

If you found the carrier bag unsatisfactory in any way, please give your reasons below:

_____

_____

_____

_____

Thank you for your help.

In order to develop a **design proposal** you need to gather information to help you make choices. Information can come from people, places, databases, books . . .

Sources of information

But you need to *sort* the information into *facts* and *opinions*.

## Fact or opinion?

**Facts** are things you can see, measure and check for yourself.
**Opinions** are people's views . . . what they like, dislike or think about things.

### *Discuss*

A group of pupils wanted to design a new school bag, so they asked other pupils for information.
Look at the answers to their **questionnaires**.
Which replies are *facts* and which are *opinions*?
How could they present their results?

Questions and results of
SCHOOL BAG SURVEY
Question 1. What type of bag do
you use for school ?
Replies: Satchel (4) Backpack (11)
Carrier bag (2) Holdall (2)
others (2)
Question 2. What is your bag
made from ?
Replies: Plastic (9) Leather (1)
Polythene (2) Cotton (2)
Mixture (7)
Question 3. What sort of bag
do you like ?
Replies: I don't like bright colours
for bags. I hate satchels. I
e fashionable bags. I don't →

School bag survey

## Recording facts

If you are collecting *facts*, such as the number of different types of school bag, you can *count* the results.

One quick way to count is called tallying.

Instead of using numbers 1, 2, . . . you can make a mark (|) called a **tally**.

The fifth mark goes across the other four.

*Results of bag survey*

| Types of bag | Tally | Total in numbers |
|---|---|---|
| satchel | \|\| \|\| | 4 |
| back pack | ⊞⊞ ⊞⊞ \| | 11 |
| holdall | \|\| | 2 |
| carrier bag | \|\| | 2 |
| others | \|\| | 2 |
| **Total number of bags** | | 21 |

## *Discuss*

For practice, conduct your own survey on school bags. You can use the questions above or invent your own. Find out *facts* and *opinions*.

Complete a *tally chart* of results which show the facts.

How could you record or present opinions?

## Opinions

Opinions are important because they consider other people's needs and views. You may find

Some people have unusual opinions

that other people's opinions give you ideas for further investigation.

To research designs for a school bag which could meet the needs of most pupils, you could ask for their *opinions* – an *opinion poll*!

## *Discuss*

In a group, imagine that you had collected the opinions about school bags above from other pupils.

You would need to gather more facts to support your design proposal.

What ideas can you develop from these opinions?

Test out your ideas in the form of a questionnaire (see page 16).

Asking questions to collect information

If you have been asked questions in the street by someone holding a clipboard, they are probably conducting a **market research** survey using a **questionnaire** (see page 16).

A market researcher at work

## Discuss and record

Discuss why market research is important when designing new products.
Use the leaflet on the right to give you ideas.
Perhaps members of your group have been interviewed by market researchers. Find out about their experiences.
Record your findings about market research.
Suggest some hints on how to organize a market research survey and ask questions. How can the results of a survey be used?

Use a dictionary or other books to find out about these words and phrases used in the leaflet.

> sample   demographic details   research
> analysis   statistical information
> anonymous and confidential

Give an example to show what they mean.

## The purpose of market research Interviewing

In Britain we expect business, industry and Government to take account of the differing needs, tastes and opinions of people. We expect our goods and services to be designed to meet the demands of the different sections of the community.

A market research survey is designed to find out the facts, so that those who influence our lives can base their decisions on facts. Only then can the food products, the transport systems, the household goods, the publications and television programmes, and the office equipment be designed to improve the quality of our lives.

### The way in which you were interviewed

In order to make sure that a representative sample was interviewed you may have been asked certain questions about your age, occupation, income and other 'demographic' details. These questions will be used in the research analysis to check the sample against other statistical information.

The questionnaire which the interviewer used will have been carefully constructed and tested by experienced researchers. The interviewer will have been instructed to read out the questions exactly as they are printed and is not allowed to change the wording to give a personal opinion. These precautions are taken to ensure that your answers are not influenced in any way by the interviewer.

So you are giving your own personal views, but these will be analysed together with the answers from all the other people interviewed and thus become totally anonymous and confidential.

*Leaflet Source:* Association of Market Survey Organisations Ltd.

Planning a market research survey

## Role play

Imagine that you are part of a market research team which wants to help a client launch a new product. Work in groups of four or five people. You need to choose people to play the roles of
- client
- market researcher
- people to be interviewed

**Hints**
- What is your new product?
- What information does the client want?
- Design a short questionnaire to use in your survey.
- Test out your questionnaire.
- Present your findings to the client.
- Write a script or make a plan to help present your role play.

Act out your market research, with people in different roles. Present your ideas to the rest of the class. Ask for their comments.

# Using a tape recorder for interviews

A tape recorder can be a great help in your design and technology work. It can help you with your research, collecting information and presenting your results.

## Discuss

Discuss in your group what a tape recorder would be useful for.

What to use a tape recorder for

## Planning to use a tape recorder

# School lunches

The lunch queue

## *Discuss*

How could a tape recorder help you with your research, collecting information and presenting your results?
Who could you interview about school lunches?

School lunches: what do people think?

## *Plan*

How would you record people's answers to your questions?
What things will you have to think about if you use a tape recorder?

## *Discuss*

Discuss in your group the things you would have to remember if you were recording an interview with someone about the school lunch queue.

### Here are some tips for interviewing

- decide who would be able to answer your question and give you the information you need. You may need to get permission from your headteacher. You may also have to make an appointment.

- make a list of the questions you want to ask and use a clipboard.

- approach the person very politely and thank them at the end.

- practise using the tape recorder first.

- if you are working as a group divide up the tasks so that one person is reading the questions whilst the other is recording the information.

Tips for interviewing

# How to observe things

Observing, or looking at things, is a useful way to get ideas and information for design proposals. Here is one example. Annabel visited a children's playground and recorded what she saw.

I sat and watched children playing in the playground for 30 minutes.
I drew a map of the playground.
I took some photos.
Notes
The swings were quite high, and there was a baby swing.
Dogs made a mess round the swings.
There is a special soft surface under the seesaw.
Kids had to wait to use the seesaw and it seemed dangerous.
Little children liked the roundabout, but older kids pushed them off.
A boy rode his BMX round the playground.

Notes on the playground

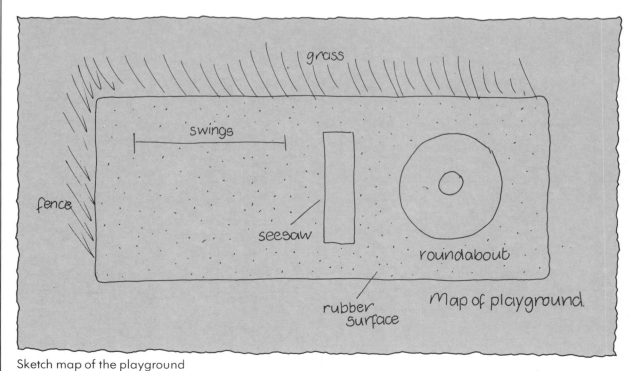

grass

swings

fence

seesaw

roundabout

rubber surface

Map of playground.

Sketch map of the playground

## Discuss

What useful information can you get from observation? Use the playground example to give you ideas. How could these notes, photo and sketch be used to develop **design proposals** – for example, for safer playgrounds?

## Test and record

Carry out an observation for yourself. It could be a place such as a playground or a group of children playing, or just a careful study of one object, such as a roundabout.

Record what you see. Compare your ideas with others. Remember, everyone sees things differently!

Think of ideas for design plays.

## Real life observation

How is observation used in real life? The Research Institute for Consumer Affairs carried out an investigation into children's playgrounds. They collected information in several ways – one method was observation.
They observed
- how many children used the equipment
- how well the equipment was looked after
- the amount of vandalism
- how children used equipment.

This is part of their report:

> Up to six children were seen on the centre piece of a see-saw, rocking it from side to side.

**Results**
Their findings were used to help make councils aware about the dangers in playgrounds, and help them with design ideas. Some of their results on equipment are given in the table at the bottom of the page.

### Do kids like playgrounds
Yes, they do. RICA asked 7- to 12-year-olds a lot of questions about the sort of things they like doing outdoors. Virtually all of them had been to a playground; going was the thing they most often thought of as a play activity.

*Source: Which?* August 1976

## Discuss

Do you think this investigation into playgrounds was necessary? Give your reasons. How do you think playgrounds could be improved? Record your ideas.

### Play equipment provided and how much it was used

| | Harrow Central | | | | Deptford | | |
| --- | --- | --- | --- | --- | --- | --- | --- |
| | number | proportion of total play spaces % | proportion of children using % | number | proportion of total play spaces % | proportion of children using % |
| flat swings | 45 | 18 | 23 | 95 | 14 | 19 |
| tyre swings | 3 | 1 | 3 | 12 | 2 | 6 |
| cradle swings | 31 | 12 | 9 | 67 | 10 | 15 |
| slides | 8 | 19 | 23 | 24 | 20 | 19 |
| climbing frames | 5 | 12 | 4 | 22 | 19 | 8 |
| see-saws | 11 | 9 | 8 | 15 | 4 | 4 |
| roundabouts | 6 | 19 | 19 | 17 | 19 | 17 |
| rocking horses/boats | – | – | – | 14 | 10 | 7 |
| plank swings | 4 | 10 | 11 | – | – | – |
| plane swings | – | – | – | 8 | 2 | 5 |

# How to make case studies

If you make a *case study* of a person, family or group, it helps to discover their views and to understand the way they live. You can use a case study to design and provide for their *needs*.

## How to carry out a case study

Here are some examples of case studies of pupils from Park House School. The *aim* was to find out their views on food. Each pupil agreed to be interviewed and the interview lasted for 5–10 minutes. Notes were made as each pupil spoke and a photograph was taken. Each case study shows only the views of the person interviewed.

### Shireen Salama aged 12

*I've been a vegetarian for nearly a year so I don't eat meat at all – I don't like animals being killed. I'm a bit health conscious – no additives or E numbers. We buy vegetarian cheese with no animal products in it and we choose food without artificial colouring.*

### Michael Kiuber aged 12

*I'm fussy about the way food looks. I like food which is presented well and is colourful, like Chinese meals. I don't eat much at home. For my packed lunch I've got six Polish sausage sandwiches and a salad, an apple, a banana and two Ribenas. I can't eat it all at lunchtime so I might eat it on the way home. Then I'm not hungry for dinner!*

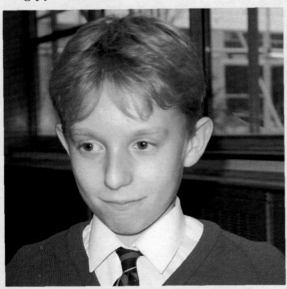

## Ideas for designs

Read the case studies and then try these ideas.
- Design some packed lunches for the week to meet each pupil's needs.
- Help design and plan a school's meals menu for this group of pupils.
- Evaluate the range of foods for sale which meet their needs.

## Design and make

Carry out your own case study. Try a short case study like the ones on these pages. Think about these points.
- What do you want to find out about the person you are interviewing?
- Get permission before you start.
- Record the interview using a tape or video.
- Write up your notes – try a word processor.
- How could you use your case study to design something for their needs?

### Emma Boisson aged 12

*I'm allergic to anything with caffeine in it – tea, coffee, cocoa, Coca Cola, chocolate cakes. When I eat food with caffeine in it makes me dizzy and I can't think straight. If I avoid these foods, I feel better. You can buy decaffeinated foods now. When my friends eat chocolate, I close my eyes because I really like it!*

### Natasha Ahmad aged 12

*Because I am a Muslim, I'm not allowed to eat pork, bacon or lard or drink wine. I have to look carefully at food labels. I usually eat vegetarian chocolates since I can't eat chocolates with animal fats. Jams and sweets like jelly babies are sometimes made with gelatine, so I can't eat them. We buy sunflower margarine and vegetarian cheese and yogurts with a tick on the label which says they're vegetarian.*

### Darren Mahoney aged 13

*Some foods make me hyperactive – sausages, drinks with colouring in them and beefburgers. I have to have a special diet with plain foods like salads, 7 Up, plain crisps, eggs and meat. Foods with additives made me do things out of control.*

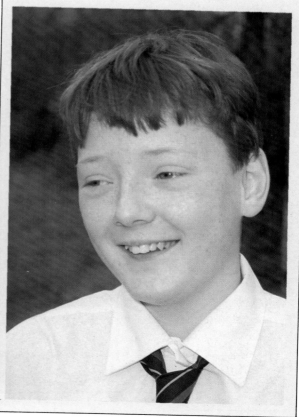

A telephone call can provide you with quick, up-to-date information, but be careful – it can be expensive!

## Hints on using a telephone

- Check the cost of your call before you dial. Local numbers are cheaper than national calls. Morning calls are the most expensive.
- What do you want to find out? Make notes before you dial. This saves time and money.
- If possible, find out the name of the person you need to speak to before you call. Keep a record of who you spoke to in case you need to call again.
- Speak clearly and be polite. Thank the people for helping you.

- Have some paper and a pencil handy to write down the information you receive.
- Answerphones are very popular these days. Plan a clear message which you can leave on the machine for people to call you back.

## Quick quiz on telephone costs

Use the leaflet *Your Guide to Telephone Charges*, September 1989 – or the latest edition, to help answer these questions.

1 If you make a local call for one minute at the following times what is the cost?
a) morning  b) afternoon  c) evening or weekends
2 What is the cost of dialling a freephone (0800) number?
3 If you called a number which was within 56 km of your local area, what would it cost at different times of the day?

# Your Guide to Telephone Charges

*Effective from September 1989*

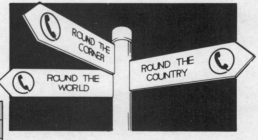

## LOCAL CALLS

| Charge Rate Period | Call Duration | | | | |
|---|---|---|---|---|---|
| | 1 min | 2 mins | 3 mins | 4 mins | 5 mins |
| Cheap Rate Mon-Fri 6pm-8am Sat & Sun all day | 5p | 5p | 5p | 5p | 5p |
| Standard Rate Mon-Fri 8am-9am 1pm-6pm | 5p | 10p | 15p | 15p | 20p |
| Peak Rate Mon-Fri 9am-1pm | 5p | 10p | 15p | 20p | 25p |

### 0800 & FREEFONE CALLS

If a number begins 0800, the call is FREE to you. A call to a FreeFone Name or a FreeFone Number is also FREE to you. Simply dial 100 and ask the operator to put your through to the FreeFone Name/Number you require.

## NATIONAL CALLS

| Type of Call and Charge Letter (note 1) | Cheap Rate Mon-Fri 6pm-8am Sat & Sun all day | | | | | Standard Rate Mon-Fri 8am-9am and 1pm–6pm | | | | | Peak Rate Mon-Fri 9am–1pm | | | | |
|---|---|---|---|---|---|---|---|---|---|---|---|---|---|---|---|
| | 1 min | 2 mins | 3 mins | 4 mins | 5 mins | 1 min | 2 mins | 3 mins | 4 mins | 5 mins | 1 min | 2 mins | 3 mins | 4 mins | 5 mins |
| National calls up to 56.4 km* outside local call area and calls to Callstream service 0055 nos – (a) | 5p | 10p | 10p | 15p | 20p | 10p | 20p | 30p | 35p | 46p | 15p | 25p | 40p | 51p | 61p |
| National calls over 56.4 km* connected over low cost routes – (b1) | 5p | 10p | 15p | 20p | 25p | 10p | 20p | 30p | 40p | 51p | 15p | 30p | 40p | 56p | 71p |
| National calls over 56.4 km*, calls to the Channel Islands, Isle of Man and calls to Callstream service 0066 nos – (b) | 10p | 15p | 20p | 30p | 35p | 15p | 25p | 40p | 51p | 66p | 20p | 35p | 51p | 71p | 86p |

© British Telecommunications plc 1989. registered office: 81 Newgate Street, London EC1A 7AJ.  Registered in England No: 1800000.

Telephone charges *Source:* British Telecommunications PLC

You can look up telephone numbers in a phone book. *Yellow Pages* is a special directory within different sections. Other directories, like *The Health calls Directory*, provide more specialized information.

Using a directory

## Role play

Imagine that the cutting below was part of a page from *Yellow Pages* in *your* area. Who could you telephone to obtain up-to-date information on waste disposal and recycling? Plan out your telephone call. In your group, act out the telephone call. Remember to make notes of what is said. How long did it take? What is the cost of your call?

## Discuss

How could you use the Healthcall service for some research? What sort of information might you seek?
Look at the cutting at the bottom of the page. Work out how much it would cost to telephone some of these numbers.

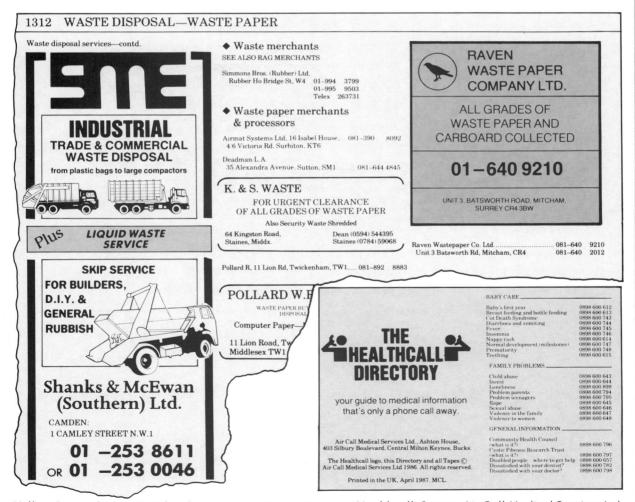

*Yellow Pages, Source:* British Telecommunications PLC

*Healthcall, Source:* Air Call Medical Services Ltd

Letter writing is an important communication skill to learn. You may need to write letters to
- ask an expert for help
- make an appointment for an interview
- ask a company for information
- arrange a visit to a shop or museum
- say 'thank you' for help given.

It is easy to make mistakes.

Here are some letter writing hints and tips.

**Pupils just don't know how to write letters today!**

Companies are complaining about the quality of letters from pupils at school. 'A lot of letters just don't make sense,' said a spokesperson. 'Pupils must be clear about what information they need – and check their spelling!'

## Arranging a visit

Keep a copy of the letter with the address where it was sent.

Mrs D Plumrose
School meals supervisor
Wessex Town Hall
Pond Road
Chalmford
Wessex WR2 6LS

Stanley Bloggs School
Furrow Lane
Great Danmow
Wessex WM2 3SR
0937 - 4864
September 14th 1990

Make sure you have a return address, postcode and telephone number.

Put a date.

If possible, find a name to write to

Dear Mrs Plumrose,
      After my telephone call today I am writing to confirm our class visit to your school meals kitchen.
Our class, 3m, has 20 pupils. We'll arrive at the central kitchens, Pudding Lane, on Thursday October 19th at 9.30 am. We expect the visit to last 1 hour. Our teacher's name is Mr Gravy.
      Please could you write or telephone to make sure everything is alright?
                  Yours Sincerely

      Tom Ridley
( TOM RIDLEY CLASS 3M )

You can handwrite, type or use a wordprocessor.

Give exact details.

Make sure they have received the letter.

Use 'sincerely' when you know the name – Mrs Plumrose Use 'faithfully' when you write 'Sir' or 'Madam'.

Sign and print your name so they can read your writing.

30

## Saying 'thank you'

Stanley Bloggs School
Furrow Lane
Great Danmow
Wessex WM2 3SR
0937-4864
October 19th 1990.

Mrs D Plumrose
School meals Supervisor
Wessex Town Hall
Pond Road
Chalmford
Wessex WR2 6LS

Dear Mrs Plumrose,
        Thank you for letting our class visit your kitchens.
We really enjoyed our visit. Perhaps you would like to come to school
to see our 'lunch ideas' Project later this year?
                Yours sincerely Tom Ridley
        (TOM RIDLEY CLASS 3M)

## A pointless letter

Inamess School
Muddle Road
Untidy town
Forsit

Dear kitchenclass,
        I'm doing a design project on kitchens Can you send me some stuff and
explain how it's done?
                Yours Darren.

## Ideas

Make a rough copy of your letter and get others
to check it. Find spelling difficult? – try a
dictionary or spell check on a computer.
*Check* your letter again before it is sent.

Print the letter using a computer.

Check your spelling on a computer.

## Design and make

In your groups design a letter.
- Will you use your school or home address?
- What is the aim of your letter – who will
  you write to and what do you want to find
  out?
- Use some of the hints and tips on letter
  writing.
- Show your letter to others and ask for their
  comments and corrections.
- Try using a typewriter or word processing
  program on the computer.

## Further ideas

You could design a display for your school on
'communicating with others' to help them with
their work.

# Getting ideas from places

The area around your home or school has many places which can provide you with ideas and information.

## Discuss

Imagine that you could visit the places on the map below to obtain ideas and information. In a group discuss how you could
- get advice on money
- watch children at play
- find out about health and fitness
- conduct a shopping survey
- find out how the elderly are looked after
- watch someone using a computer
- find an expert on road safety.

Suggest ways of using the places you have not included. Record your findings.

## Research and record

Work in pairs or in a group and think about your area. It could be the area around your school or where you live. What places could you visit to get ideas, information and advice? Where could you conduct surveys?
Record your findings – you could draw a map or make a **'Resources'** list. Compare your ideas with others. Could you add more details? You could store this **data** on a computer.

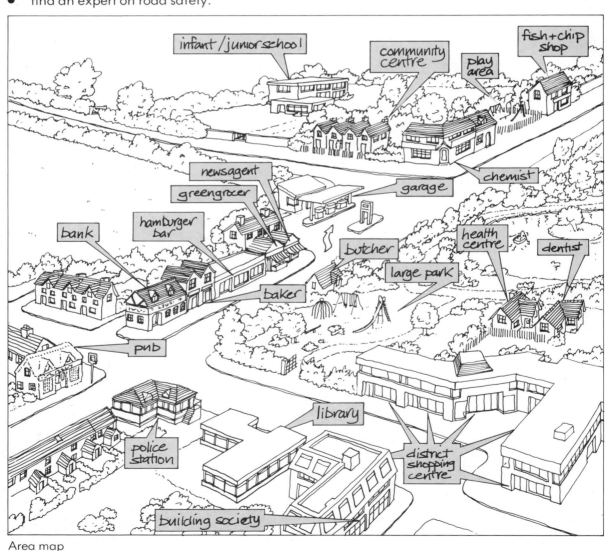

Area map

## What about getting 'design' ideas?

How can you get 'design' ideas by just looking at a map or visiting an area? You could think about kinds of information and ideas you might get from, for example banks and building societies. You will certainly get some advice on money! How then could you develop a design proposal? **Brainstorm** (see page 14) your group!

Another way is to think about the *needs* of the people in the area.

*Spider diagram of ideas.*

The needs of people in an area. How can the area help?

### *Discuss and record*

How can an area like your own or the one shown on the map provide for people's needs? Choose one of the people or groups above. How could you meet these people's needs? The example for the need 'I need company' may help you to start off.

'I need company'
- Perhaps we could plan to visit some elderly people?
- The local retirement home might like to come to school for tea.
- We could find out what goes on in our area.

Pupils at Aspen House School wanted to design some puppets. They needed to do some research and decided to get some help from the experts in the Horniman Museum. This is how they set about organizing their visit.

**Step 1**    If we are going to design a puppet, who can we ask to help us?

**Step 2**    We'll have to get permission to ask them.

**Step 3**    Now we'll have to write a letter to the museum to arrange a visit next week – or we could ring.

**Step 4**    'Hello Mr Mahoney, just ringing to confirm our visit next week.'

**Step 5**    We'd better decide what we need to take.

**Step 6**    Let's work out what questions we need to ask.

**Step 7**   Let's find the quickest way to get there – we've only got an hour.

**Step 8**   Here we are at last.

**Step 9**   The expert shows us a puppet.

**Step 10**   This is how a shadow puppet works.

**Step 11**   Let's try out a puppet for ourselves!

## Plan

Plan a visit that you could make in your area. Use the photos to help you make a checklist of the things you will need to remember.

Using a library

## Discuss

Work in pairs or in a group. Imagine that you need to use the library in the picture to carry out some research.

Talk about how you would go about looking up information. You could choose a topic such as puppets, parties or your own idea to help you focus your discussion. How could you get advice and help? Where would you find up-to-date information? What useful **equipment** is found in a library?

## Research

*Test* out your ideas by visiting a real library. *Record* your findings. You may want to draw a plan of the library and label useful areas.

## Evaluate

Compare your library with the one in the picture. Which do you prefer and why? Record your **evaluation**.

## Design and make

Design and make something to help other pupils use a library effectively for their research. An idea for a game is given below. For your design plan, think about
- how to find things in libraries
- looking up information in dictionaries and encyclopaediae
- the Dewey system for cataloguing books
- using an index and catalogue.

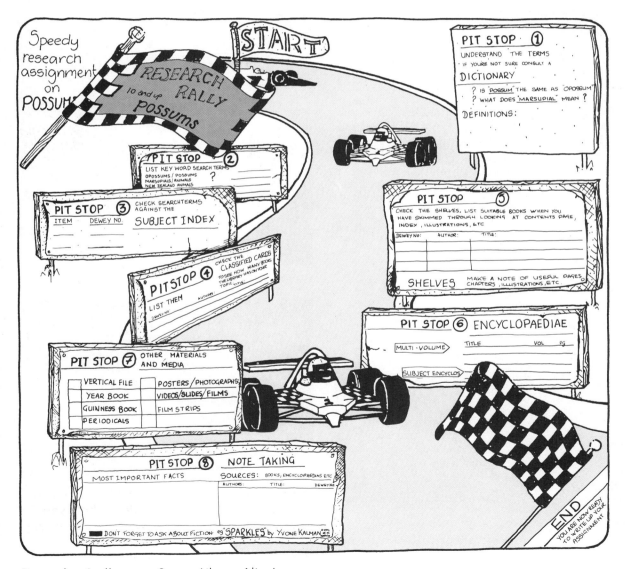

Researchers' rally game *Source*: Library Alive!

## Discuss

How often do you use the television to get information? Think of a topic and **brainstorm** your group (see page 14) to get ideas on how to use a TV. The programme guide might help.

## Teletext

Teletext is an information service on the television. BBC call their teletext *Ceefax* and the system for ITV is called *Oracle*. You need a television set equipped with a special decoder to receive pages of teletext. Pages are transmitted from a computer and provide up to the minute information on many subjects.

## Research and record

Find out how to use Ceefax and Oracle. Here is one idea. Imagine that you have the chance to leave your school or home immediately to set off on a holiday to Europe. You can go anywhere you please, but you must make travel arrangements *now*!

Use a suitably equipped TV.
- Call up the Travel sections of Ceefax or Oracle.
- Look at the weather pages to decide where you are going.

- How will you travel – train, bus, ship, air? Sort out details.
- Check on travel delays.
- Check through your plans once more.
- Record your findings

## Other databases

In your local library or at school you can probably use a **database** called Campus 2000 or Prestel to get information. Using the computer you can be connected through the telephone exchange to a vast amount of data stored in computers.

Using Campus 2000

Climates in European cities on Oracle *Source:* Oracle, ITV

Travel news

Ways Campus 2000 can help.

## Research and evaluate

Search out your nearest Campus 2000 (Prestel) database. It could be at school or in the local library. Ask permission to use it. Find out what leisure activities are on in your area for yourselves or a disabled person. Report on your findings to others in your class. How useful was the database? Was it easy to use? Write a short **evaluation**.

## Discuss

Where can you get up-to-date written information about food safety?

## Skimming for information

It is not always necessary to read a whole page or article to find the facts you need. As you read a page, your eye will catch certain words or phrases which are important. Jot down brief notes as you read.

## Record

**Skim** the article on 'The chilling facts of safe home cooking'. Make some brief notes.

**Helpful hints**
- What information is given on buying and using chilled food?
- How should a fridge, freezer, and microwave oven be used for safety?
- How does the author suggest you can avoid food poisoning?
- Why is the Checklist box useful?

---

# The chilling facts of safe home cooking

PICTURE the average household before their evening meal. Has mum cooked it? No, she's just come in from work – she'll get a ready-prepared meal out of the fridge just for herself. The family no longer eats together because it can rely on today's high-tech food any time they want it. The fridge is bulging with chicken tikka, lasagne, chicken supreme and ready-washed salads. Dad will take his pick when he gets home – even he has learnt how to use the microwave. As for the teenage children – if they eat at all they will want to do so quickly and conveniently probably in front of the television. They have never learnt to cook.

Wherever the truth lies, it would be helpful if we understood more about this new sort of food. Chilled food is food which has been prepared – often cooked – chilled and then kept between 0°C and 3°C just

PETER BAZALGETTE
and GABRIELLE
O'CONNOR on how to
avoid listeria hysteria

above freezing. It is crucial that these temperatures are then maintained, whether in the factory, during transportation or in a shop's chiller cabinet.

Food tends to be three to five days from preparation, but all are potential breeding grounds for listeria if poorly prepared. Much of the listeria found in the surveys would have been killed when the food was heated at home. But the most worrying products are those which will not be reheated – chilled roast chicken, for instance, or coleslaw, which was responsible for a serious outbreak in the US.

Despite the failure of the high-tech kitchen to compensate for our

low level of skills, commonsense is still a powerful corrective.

Checklist of simple dos and don'ts, compiled with the help of David Edwards of the Food Hygiene Bureau:
● Don't buy cooked-chilled food outside the "sell-by" date, and eat it by the "use-by" date.
● Buy cooked-chilled food from reputable shops which show an awareness of hygiene.
● Buy chilled foods at the end of shopping expeditions and get them home to the fridge as soon as possible, particularly in summer.
● Check that your fridge is working properly.
● Follow the cooking instructions and ensure your reheating is thorough.

*Source: The Sunday Times*, 22 January 1989

# Getting at the facts

Charts containing **data** can provide valuable information.

| Chart A – Gastro-intestinal infections (England & Wales): 1981–1988 | | | | | |
|---|---|---|---|---|---|
| | *1981* | *1983* | *1985* | *1987* | *1988* |
| Salmonella | 11 500 | 14 500 | 12 500* | 18 000 | 24 000 |
| Campylobacter | 13 000 | 17 500 | 23 500 | 28 000 | 29 500 (est) |
| Listeria | 80 | 120 | 150 | 260 | 290 |

*Reduction attributed to cold summer

*Source:* Diane Roberts – 'Food Preparation – the fault that led to food-borne disease' – Proceedings of the XIII International Congress of Nutrition

## Chart B – Where food poisoning occurs (Roberts) 1982 & 1985

| Location | % outbreaks |
|---|---|
| **1985** | |
| Restaurant/Hotel | 19.0 |
| Banquet/Reception | 8.0 |
| Hospital/Similar Institutions | 15.0 |
| Schools | 14.0 |
| Colleges/Similar Institutions | 2.0 |
| **Sub total for Mass Catering** | **58.0** |
| Home Catering | 1.0 |
| Other | 4.0 |
| Shops/Bakeries/Takeaways*/ Milk Rounds | 15.0 |
| Family Homes | 14.0 |
| Scombrotoxin | 8.0 |

*Takeaway shops would probably be considered 'Catering'.

*Source:* EAG Scientific Report May 1989, 'Salmonella and Listeria'

But we keep everything in the fridge!
Bacteria can multiply in the fridge and contaminate other food if it isn't stored correctly.

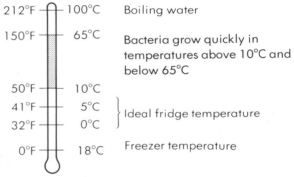

| | | |
|---|---|---|
| 212°F | 100°C | Boiling water |
| 150°F | 65°C | Bacteria grow quickly in temperatures above 10°C and below 65°C |
| 50°F | 10°C | |
| 41°F | 5°C | } Ideal fridge temperature |
| 32°F | 0°C | |
| 0°F | 18°C | Freezer temperature |

Thermometer drawing

## Discuss

How can you use the information on food safety and hygiene to generate a **design proposal?**
**Brainstorm** your group to get ideas.

## Record

Practise *extracting information* from data.
The 'consumer' has been blamed for outbreaks of food poisoning. Has the number of food poisoning cases increased in recent years?
Use chart A and make notes to answer this question.
What does chart B tell you about where food poisoning outbreaks occur? Do you think the consumer is to blame? Make brief notes.
You can extract information from drawings too.
Look at the thermometer drawing.
How can the information be used to give advice to a consumer on how to store food safely?

> We could make a video to show how people can look after food safely.

> We could observe people cooking and show them how to improve.

> Or make some posters for school.

Food Safety
*Source:* Food Sense

41

When you carry out a survey using a **questionnaire**, you collect **data** – facts and figures. In order to understand your research, this data needs to be sorted and presented so that it is easy to understand. You could present your findings to others using a large display. Data can look really boring. On this page are some fun ways of presenting information.

## Evaluate

What do you think about these different ways of presenting real life data? Record your views. How do you think the presentation could be improved? Try it for yourself.

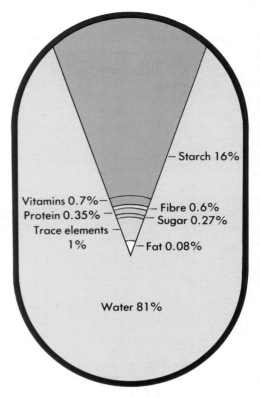

Chemical/nutrient composition of the raw potato
*Source*: Potatoes study pack

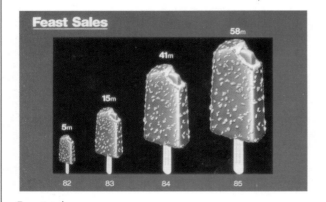

Feast sales
*Source: Wall's 1986 Report*

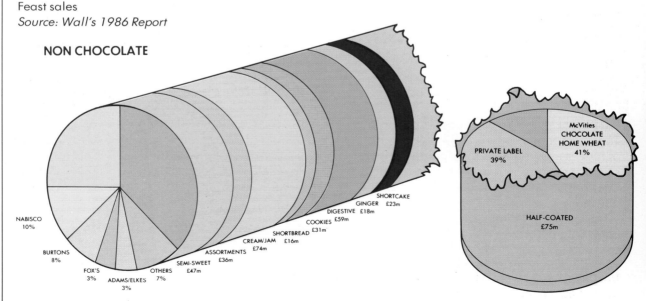

Sales of biscuits
*Source: Nabisco View of the Biscuit Market*, The Jacobs Bakery Limited

## Design and make

Suggest ways to present this Pocket Money Survey to make it more interesting. **Brainstorm** to get as many ideas as possible, try them out and discuss the results. Which do you prefer and why?

| Average weekly pocket money 1990/89 | | | | | | | |
|---|---|---|---|---|---|---|---|
| Year | Total | Boys | Girls | 5–7 | 8–10 | 11–13 | 14–16 |
| 1986 | 117p | 120p | 114p | 54p | 77p | 142p | 198p |
| 1987 | 116p | 112p | 120p | 42p | 76p | 143p | 212p |
| 1988 | 123p | 125p | 122p | 54p | 95p | 147p | 212p |
| 1989 | 140p | 143p | 136p | 65p | 97p | 167p | 274p |
| 1990 | 149p | 151p | 147p | 74p | 99p | 184p | 285p |
| % change 1990/1989 | +6% | +6% | +8% | +14% | +2% | +10% | +4% |

*Source:* Wall's Pocket Money Monitor by Gallup, Birds Eye Wall's Limited

## Averages

When you collect a large amount of data, such as the pocket money **survey** above, you may want to show what a typical pupil receives each week. An average of a set of numbers is a typical value which represents the whole group. The common average is the *mean,* and is the total of all the values divided by the number of values.

How can you find out the average weekly pocket money of 10 pupils?

| Weekly pocket money received by 10 and 11 year olds | |
|---|---|
| Pupil's number | Amount |
| 1 | £1.00 |
| 2 | £1.20 |
| 3 | £1.00 |
| 4 | £1.50 |
| 5 | £1.30 |
| 6 | £1.10 |
| 7 | £1.50 |
| 8 | £2.00 |
| 9 | £1.50 |
| 10 | £2.00 |

What's an average?

## Design and make

Conduct a survey to find out the average amount of pocket money which a particular age group receives. Interview 10–20 people. How do your results compare with the Wall's survey?

Look at the table on the right. To find the average or mean amount of pocket money of these pupils you need to find the sum (total) of *all* the money and divide it by the number of pupils.

Sum of all the pocket money = £14.10
Number of pupils = 10
Average amount of pocket money = £14.10 ÷ 10
= £1.41

# Presenting your results 2

If you have carried out a **survey** using a **questionnaire** (see page 16), you will have collected **data** – that is, **facts** and figures. How can you present this information so that others can understand it?

Daniel conducted a short food survey. He used the survey program and drew up a questionnaire.

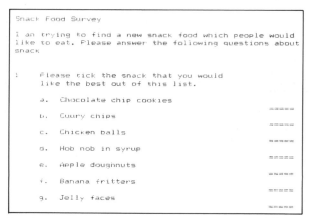

Food survey

He input his responses. The computer was able to present his results in different ways.

The first result shows the number of *respondents* to each question – the number of people who answered.

| Responses | No. of respondents |
|-----------|--------------------|
| a | 1 |
| b | 3 |
| c | 0 |
| d | 0 |
| e | 5 |
| f | 6 |
| g | 0 |

Respondents

Next the computer generated a **bar chart** of the results.

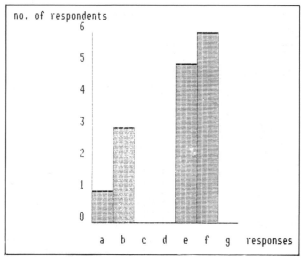

Bar chart of results

The computer also sorted the results into percentages and drew a **pie chart**.

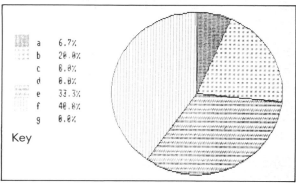

| a | 6.7% |
| b | 20.0% |
| c | 0.0% |
| d | 0.0% |
| e | 33.3% |
| f | 40.0% |
| g | 0.0% |

Key

The pie chart *Source:* The SURVEY Computer Program © ILECC Survey

A pie chart gets its name because it looks like the slices of a pie. You can compare the size of the slices – called *sectors* – at a glance. Pie charts can be very difficult to draw. A computer can do it easily.

# Presenting data

Bar charts are one of the easiest ways of displaying data. You can use a computer for speed or draw them by hand, using squared paper if possible. Here are some tips for drawing your own bar chart.

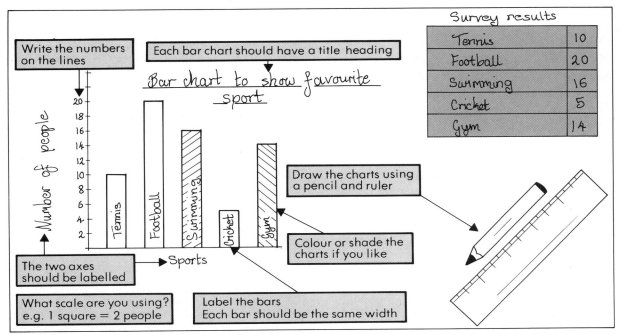

Drawing a bar chart

## Other ways of presenting data
Data can be presented on a graph.
On the right are two graphs showing the *average* amount of pocket money that teenagers in the UK receive. They are based upon the following data.

| Pocket money analysis for the UK | | | | | |
|---|---|---|---|---|---|
| Age | 12 | 13 | 14 | 15 | 16 |
| Average in £ per week | 2.30 | 2.78 | 3.48 | 4.31 | 8.99 |

*Source:* Halifax *Quest* Club Magazine Questionnaire 1989

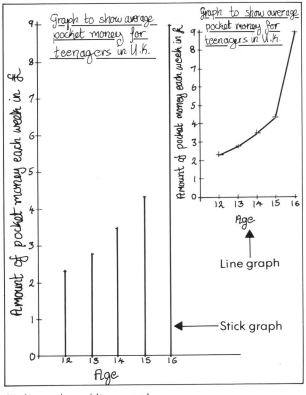

Stick graph and line graph

45

From your **surveys,** you may have collected **facts** which you can present as **bar charts** or **pie charts**.
You may also have collected **opinions**.

How can you sort out a collection of different people's views and opinions so that you can draw some *conclusions* about your survey?

The group wanted to design a booklet on 'How to cope with homework'. They conducted a survey and collected some views from other pupils on how they organized themselves when they did their homework. Here are the results.

1  You need to do all your homework before you watch TV.
2  I have my tea then start my work.
3  I think you should relax and have fun after school, then do some work.
4  I start my homework after the 6 o'clock news.
5  I think it is better to get homework done before anything else.
6  You can work with a friend, but homework must be done on time.
7  We get changed, have tea, watch a little TV then homework.
8  Homework should always be done as soon as possible.
9  I think homework is a nuisance.
10  I have tea, then start my homework whilst I watch TV.

## *Discuss*

How could you sort out these different views on when to do your homework?

To sort out these opinions you could complete statements such as:
Most pupils think that homework should be done . . .
However, a few think that . . .

What conclusions could you draw from the results of this survey?
Record your findings.

## Real surveys

In 1989, *Which?* carried out a survey to find out the views of 2450 people on buying 'green' products which are less harmful to the environment. The report draws some conclusions from the survey, and displays some results as a bar chart.

### YOUR VIEWS ON 'GREEN' PRODUCTS

● Nearly 90% said they think about the environmental effects of products when they buy and use them, at least some of the time.
● About 80% said they'd be prepared to pay extra for products which are less harmful to the environment.
● CFC-free aerosols were the most commonly-bought 'green' product; of members who considered the environment when shopping, 76% buy these. Next came recycled paper and paper products (31%), unleaded petrol (27%), organic fruit and vegetables (22%), phosphate-free detergents (14%), and paper products which aren't chlorine-bleached (14%).
● But while members were keen to buy products which are less harmful to the environment, 88% of them thought that shops were not doing enough to promote such products.

*Source: Which?* September 1989

## *Questions*

Look closely at the statements from the survey, and the bar chart.
How could you answer the following?
● Do *most* people in the survey think about the environmental effects of the products they buy?   Yes ☐   No ☐
● Are *most* people prepared to pay extra for these products?   Yes ☐   No ☐
● What do the *majority* (the most) of people think about shops and 'green' products?
Record your answers.
Use your answers to help you write a sentence to explain the conclusions of this survey.

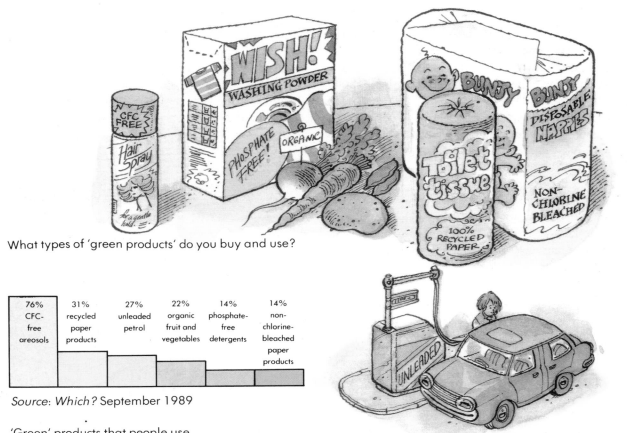

What types of 'green products' do you buy and use?

| 76% CFC-free areosols | 31% recycled paper products | 27% unleaded petrol | 22% organic fruit and vegetables | 14% phosphate-free detergents | 14% non-chlorine-bleached paper products |

*Source: Which?* September 1989

'Green' products that people use

## Percentages

Some **data,** such as this *Which?* report, is shown as percentages. A percentage is a fraction of 100.

If 5 out of 20 pupils like football, this is $\frac{5}{20}$.
How can $\frac{5}{20}$ be expressed as a fraction of 100?

$$\frac{5}{20} = \frac{\boxed{?}}{100}$$

$$\frac{5 \times 5}{20 \times 5} = \frac{25}{100}$$

The answer is $\frac{25}{100}$ or $25\%$

## *Record*

A group wanted to design a sports bag, so they interviewed 20 pupils to find out the most popular sports.
Here are their results.

| football | swimming | tennis | basket ball | other |
|----------|----------|--------|-------------|-------|
| 5 | 8 | 4 | 2 | 1 |

How could they present this data to show the results as percentages?
Try expressing the other results of this sports survey as percentages.

25% like football, but what about tennis...?

47

You can use a camera, video or cine camera to help you to investigate, to record your findings and to present your work. Remember a picture says a thousand words and a film can be looked at many times.

A camera or video might be useful to
- investigate a playgroup to see how young children play
- record your results as a tape slide programme or short video programme
- record an expert showing you a new skill which you can look at afterwards and follow
- present results of a survey about your community, for example
- record a visit
- try out a role play.

## Discuss

Think of other uses for a camera or video.

## School lunch queue

A school lunch queue

If you wanted to investigate and improve your school lunch queuing system you could keep a record using photographs or a video camera. They can help your research and you can use them to present your results.

Investigating the system

## Discuss

If you were trying to improve your lunch queuing system how would you be able to use a camera or video to help you? Use the pictures to give you ideas.

## Plan

You must have a clear idea of what you want to photograph or video otherwise you will waste film. Plan out the photographs or film you would like to take. What things will you need to think about? The diagrams will help you.

## Discuss

Discuss in your group why a video is useful and when you could use it to help you with designing.

Using a video

**Using a camera**

How much will a film cost?

How many shots am I taking?

Have I made a list of shots I want to take?

Do I need to book a camera?

Will I need a flash?

Do I want slides or prints?

What type of camera do I need?

**Using a video camera**

Do I need permission?

How much will it cost?

Who will view it?

Will I need help with organizing or filming?

What equipment will I need?

Where will I shoot my video?

Pupils at Aspen House School wanted to celebrate the Chinese Dragon Boat Festival. They decided to make decorations for the festival in a group.

The **constraints** (or limits) on the group are described below.

## 1   Time
They needed to finish the decorations in time for the festival.

## 2   Skills
They had to find out what they could do and what new skills they needed to learn. They had to share their skills with each other.

## 3   Customs
Their design had to reflect the Chinese Dragon Boat Festival.

### The Chinese Dragon Boat Festival

The Chinese Dragon Boat Festival is held around Midsummer's Day. In China local towns have races in rowing boats, each with a dragon head carved on the front. Some people believed that the dragon was a water god and rain was caused by dragons fighting in the clouds. They tried to bring rain for their growing crops by holding dragon fights between the boats.

Chinese Dragon Boat Festival

## 4   Materials and tools
They were limited to the **materials** and tools available in the school and they only had a little extra money to buy other materials.

*I can use a sewing machine*

*I'm good at drawing patterns*

*We'll have to help each other*

Sharing skills

Materials and tools

Here are their results.

The finished cushions

## Discuss

Imagine your group wants to celebrate a festival.
Which festival would you choose?

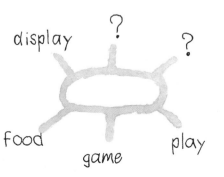

A Dragon dancer celebrates Chinese New Year

**Brainstorm** your group (see page 14) and get ideas for a **design proposal**.

Ideas

What are the constraints on your design proposal?

We'll have to use this colour

Constraints

Record your findings and present your ideas to another group. Ask for their comments.

Presenting your ideas

## Working safely together

In school practical rooms it is important to work safely. The Government report called *Safety in Practical Studies* says

> If young people are trained to develop a sense of responsibility for the safety of themselves and others, the toll of unnecessary accidents can be reduced.

*Source*: HMSO

**How can members of your class help each other to work safely together?**

## *Research*

How can you find out how to work safely in schools?
- Use the report to help you find information.
- Investigate and **observe** the dangerous areas of practical rooms.
- Look at the instructions on the equipment you will use.
- Ask an expert – a teacher in a practical room – or phone the local education authority to get information.

Let's look at the advice given in the Government report.

- Every department must have safety rules that are understood and observed.
- Unsuitable dress, certain types of footwear, long hair and jewellery may be dangerous.

- Organization – clutter must be avoided – floor areas must be free from clothes, bags and rubbish.
- Electrical equipment – manufacturer's operating instructions should be obtained and the pupils should read and follow directions.
- To avoid the dangers of food poisoning ... hands should be washed, clean protective clothing worn ... work surfaces should be smooth and clean ...
- First aid – fully equipped first aid kits should be ... kept in easily accessible places.
- Fire: staff and pupils should know how to use the fire appliances. Fire drills are necessary.

## *Discuss*

Use the **pie charts** which compare the accidents in school practical rooms with home accidents.

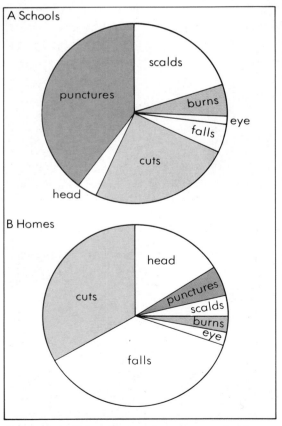

Accidents in Home Economics rooms and at home
*Source*: ILEA

Are school practical rooms safer places than the home? Explain your answer. What are the main causes of accidents in practical rooms? How do you think they could be avoided? Record your findings.

From your research, discuss ways of helping pupils work safely in practical rooms.

## Design and make

From your research, design and make something which would help other pupils work safely together in practical rooms.

We could draw up a list of safety rules and maybe print out a chart.

RULES OK.

We could use a computer to design special clothes for practicals.

We need to check out where we can put our bags and coats.

Maybe we need some hooks.

We could observe what other pupils do and suggest improvements

We could make some cards for each *piece* of equipment to show how it must be used safely.

Electricity is serious

We could show how to help a person injured from electrical shock.

Let's find out what should be in a first aid kit.

And how to use it.

We could draw a map of where the kits are kept in the school.

We could give the whole school a talk on the use of fire equipment.

And test out the fire drill from our practical room.

Ways of working safely

# Planning your work

Every day we have to plan our time in order to get things done. Important tasks must come first. For example, it is necessary to complete your homework for the next day. Less important things – like watching 'Neighbours' – can wait! This is called **prioritizing tasks** – sorting them into order of importance.

Sometimes you can find ways to fit everything in. For example, you could record 'Neighbours' on the video and watch it after doing your homework. Getting to school on time needs a well organized *plan* – a **system** for doing things. How is your system planned for arriving at school on time? Here are some of the things you may have to do.

getting up

getting washed

getting dressed

having breakfast

brushing hair and teeth

putting on coat/shoes

picking up bags

arriving at school on time

Things you may have to do

You may have other tasks in the morning before school.

paper round

helping an elderly relative

helping to do the washing up

taking younger kids to school

Jobs you may have to do

## Plan

Work in pairs or in a group. Show how you plan your morning before you arrive at school. You could draw up a *timeplan*, *flow chart* or just make a *list* to show the order of things you do.

| Time | Order of work |
|------|---------------|
| 7.00 | Get up and wash |
| 7.15 | Make cup of tea for dad |
| 7.30 | Have breakfast |

**Timeplan**

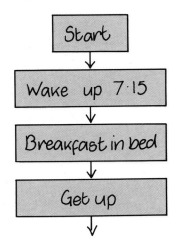

**Flowchart**

1. Get up at 5.30 am.

2. Get dressed and leave house

3. Paper round for 1 hour

4. 6.45 have breakfast

**List**

## Evaluate

Swap your plan with someone else. Compare and discuss each plan. Is the plan *effective*? Do you arrive on time and are you well organized to begin the day? Could your system be improved? Present your plans to others and ask for their views.

## Role play

Act out the scene of a pupil arriving late for school. Someone could play the pupil, another the teacher, and others pretend to be friends. Find out why the pupil is late and offer advice and help.

## Making plans

Through this piece of work, you may have discovered that there are many ways of ordering tasks to make a *plan*. The plan should work and be *effective* to meet its aim. In this case, the aim was to arrive, well organized, on time for school. Poorly organized plans often don't work so the aim may not be met. So, pupils arrive late for school.

## Design and make

Pupils starting at a new school often need advice on how to plan and organize themselves. Design and make something to help them. Think about what advice could be given and how it could be presented.
- handouts
- a talk
- video
- computer game

Design and make your idea then test it out on other pupils and ask them to **evaluate** the results.

One of the oldest and quickest ways in the world to describe something is to draw it! Think of prehistoric cave drawings and Aborigine designs.

An Aborigine design

**Sketches** and drawings liven up design work and help you to develop your design ideas. Sketches are quickly drawn in pencil or pen. Drawings, plans and diagrams take longer and may be coloured or labelled.

**Using sketches, plans and models**
Many schools have problems with the design of their cloakrooms and lockers.

## Research and discuss

What are the problems with the lockers and cloakrooms in your school?

## Plan

You want to improve the cloakroom and lockers in your school. To do this you could look at lockers in and out of school and **sketch** some ideas for improving the design of the lockers.

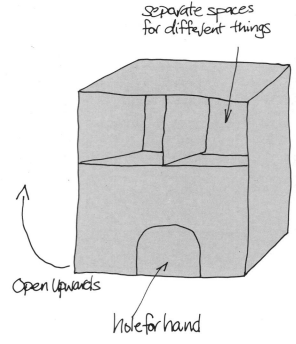

separate spaces for different things

Open upwards

hole for hand

Sketch of a locker

Now you can use drawings, plans and models to develop your ideas and to find ways to solve these problems.

You will need to draw a **scale plan** of the cloakroom with detailed measurements. Draw the pieces of furniture to scale and move them around the plan to see if you can improve the design of the cloakroom.

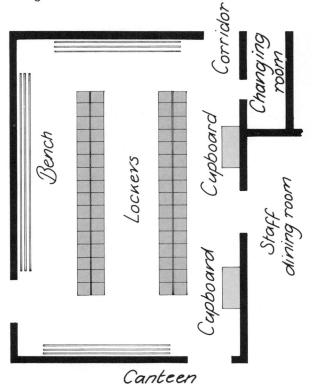

A scale plan, scale 1:50

You could draw **diagrams** like the ones given to show how the new lockers are going to look and what **materials** you will need.

## Design and make

Now design and make a **model** of the locker out of scrap cardboard to show what your final design will look like.

Making a model of the locker

## Evaluate

Show the models and working diagrams to other pupils and ask for their comments on the design.

## Discuss

Think of your school. What else could you design and make which would need sketches, plans, working diagrams or models to help with the designing?

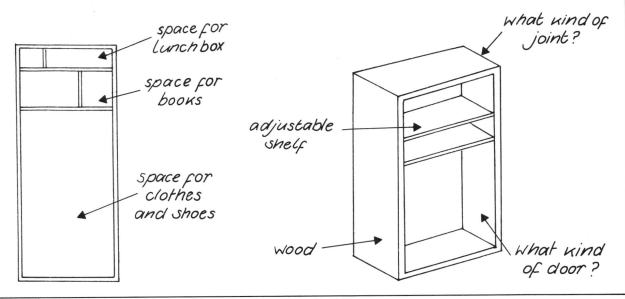

space for lunch box

space for books

space for clothes and shoes

what kind of joint?

adjustable shelf

wood

what kind of door?

# Choosing materials

When you make something – be it biscuits, bags or bicycles – you need to decide which **materials** will work the best.

*Which materials would you use?*

## Discuss

Imagine that your group wants to make a *biscuit, bag* or *bicycle*. Which materials would you use to make one of these **artefacts**? Discuss and record what you chose and why you made the choices.

Biscuits, bags, bicycles

## Properties of materials

When you choose materials, you need to think about their *properties* – how they behave and can be used.

## Discuss

What is meant by *the properties of materials*?

The artefacts illustrated on this page use a variety of different materials. Discuss what materials could be used to make each of them and decide what properties are needed for each design.

## Other matters

Here are some other things to think about when choosing materials.

**Purpose** What do you want the materials to do?

**Safety** Are they safe to use?

**Cost** Can you afford to use them? Could you buy them cheaper elsewhere? Would a less expensive material work as well?

**Availability** Are the materials easy to find or buy?

**Aesthetics** How does it look – does it give a good result?

Artefacts using various materials

## Discuss

What materials would you choose to make one of the following?
- a child's toy
- packed lunch for a vegetarian
- a desk tidy

What materials would you avoid and why?
Describe four *properties* of the materials which would help with your design.
How could you test the materials to see if they meet your design requirements? Record your ideas and compare them with others.

# Choosing equipment

When you are designing and making something at school, you have to think about the **materials** and **equipment** you will need to complete the work. To be well organized, it is good idea to make a list of the things you will need.

Do you have the necessary skills to carry out the work? If not, how will you learn these skills?

You could make a planning list of the materials, equipment and skills you think you will need, then discuss this with your teacher.

The planning list

## Plan and discuss

Imagine that your group wants to design and make some puppets for a play, which you have written yourselves. How would you decide what equipment and skills you need? Think about the sorts of puppets you want to make.

Puppets

- What materials will you need?

- What equipment might you need?

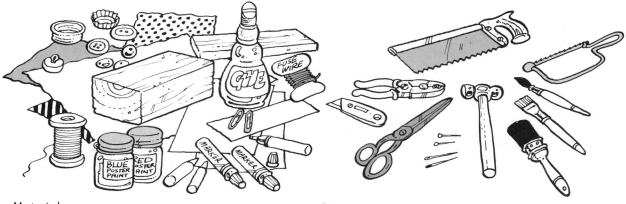

Materials

Equipment

● What special equipment might you need?

Special equipment

● What skills do you need to carry out the work?

*Can you use a sewing machine?*

*Can you use the design program on the computer?*

*Do you know about safe working in the technology room?*

Skills

## Record

Discuss and record the materials, equipment and skills needed if you wanted to make one of the following.
● a school magazine   ● a child's birthday cake
● a baby's mobile   ● a coloured kite

Make up a *planning list* to show what materials, equipment and skills you need. Show your list to your teacher and ask for comments.
What new skills might you have to learn in order to carry out the work?

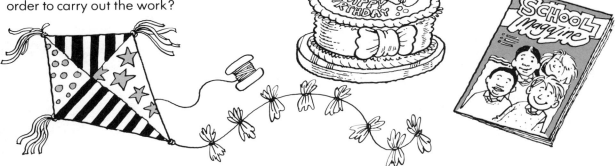

The design ideas

# Adapting things — making changes

Everyone needs to adapt and make changes as they work.

## Discuss and record

The drawings on these pages show some problems you might face if you were researching or making something.
Choose one problem and discuss it in a group.
How would you adapt and make changes to get results?
Present your ideas to the rest of the class.

> Our teacher says we can only afford to take three photos, not the five photos we had planned

> One of our group keeps arguing and not sharing the workload. What can we do?

> We need to write a neat letter, but all the computers are booked HELP!

> The fabric we have bought is really poor quality and doesn't suit our needs HELP!

> The photocopier has broken down and we need copies of our questionnaire to survey 20 people

OUT OF ORDER

> We want to test out six cake recipes, but our teacher says the food is too expensive. How can we make changes?

Possible problems

I've lost a folder full of design sketches and there are only two weeks until I must present my work. What can I do?

We must learn to use a sewing machine and a word processor, but the teacher is too busy. Where can we get help?

There are only two weeks left to complete our design and carry out the evaluation. What tasks are important to finish?

## Evaluate

Think of a real life situation when you have had to make changes in order to get things done. How successful were you? How could you have adapted your plans?

## Making masks

Billy Nicholas is a professional mask maker who visits schools and runs mask making workshops. He often only has two days in which to design and make the masks and there are many pupils in the class. How has he adapted his ideas to meet the constraints of time, cost and the skills of the pupils he works with?

*In my last workshop we designed masks around several themes – rubbish people who lived in the dump, insects and aliens. I have to use materials which produce quick and interesting results. Papier mâché is sticky and messy and takes too long to dry. Card is too stiff to make interesting masks. I use a thin foam which we cut into shapes and model pieces into ears, noses and other features, then a quick glue like Evostick which dries in 15 minutes so we can get on. We need a special mixture of PVA glue and poster paint to paint on the masks. Other paints peel off and spoil the finish. The masks don't have to be perfect – I'm just pleased if everyone is happy.*

Billy Nicholas with a selection of masks

# Costing things out

All designers need to be aware of how much things cost to make. In business, designers need to know about the costs of **materials**, *labour* and *overheads*. They also need to know how much their design will *sell for*, and how much *profit* they are expected to make.

When you make an **artefact** such as a toy, game or recipe at school, funds are usually limited, so you must cost things out carefully.

## Finding out how much things cost

- Visit shops or markets and record your findings.
- Your local council may collect 'best buys'.
- Use computerized shop receipts.
- Use computer databases.

## Working out the cost of materials

### Plan

Imagine that your group has decided to make 10 copies of a 30 page booklet. Use the costings below to work out how much you will spend on materials and extra costs such as photocopying and binding the book together. Add costs of your own materials.
How will you plan and display your costs? Will you use
- a price list
- a spreadsheet?

*Create a database on the computer*

## Using the computer

You can create a **database** on the computer which can store the costs of different materials and **equipment** for later use.

| 1 | costing kitchen equipment | |
| 2 | | |
| 3 | large electrical/gas | |
| 4 | | |
| 5 | washer—Hoover | |
| | | £274.95 |
| 6 | cooker—Creda | £349.99 |
| 7 | dryer—Philips | £69.99 |
| 8 | dishwasher—Hoover | £339.99 |
| 9 | fridge—Lec | £209.99 |
| 10 | | |
| 11 | total | £1244.87 |

## Avoiding wastage

You can save money by careful planning. Try and avoid *wastage* of materials.
Don't waste food or other materials

GLUE STICK £2·20

STRONG GLUE £3·90

PAPER GLUE 60p.

STICKY LABELS 50p for 40

CLEAR COVERING FILM 100cm – £1·00

SELLOTAPE £1 for 25m

A4 PAPER 75p for 50 SHEETS.

MARKER PENS 75p. EACH

LETRASET £7·50 A SHEET

GUMMED PAPER 9p. PER SHEET.

PHOTOCOPYING 10p a page.

COLOURED CARD A4 20p. a sheet

MY BOOK

BINDING 30 PAGES TOGETHER £1·00

MY BOOK

COLOURED A4 PAPER 6p. a sheet

Costing the materials

64

# Using a graph to help

If you need to work out the cost of various amounts of the same materials a *graph* can give you speedy results (see page 44).

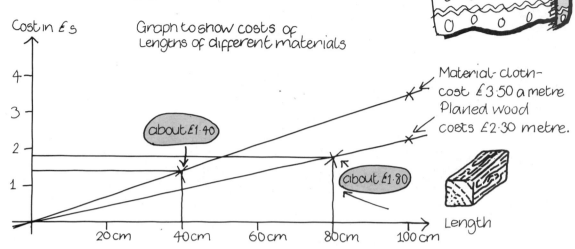

Cost in £s

Graph to show costs of Lengths of different materials

4 —
3 —
2 —
1 —

about £1·40

about £1·80

Material cloth — cost £3·50 a metre
Planed wood costs £2·30 metre.

Length

20cm   40cm   60cm   80cm   100cm

Costing wood and fabric

# Costing things out in business

When you buy goods in shops or restaurants, why do they cost more than things you could make yourself?

**Cost of a T-shirt**
Made by you!
Cost of materials, thread, electricity for machining and pressing

**Cost of a ready-made T-Shirt**
Cost of materials, thread
Cost of machinery
Wages for pattern cutters, designers, machinists
Costs of quality control and advice
Pressing and packing
Specially designed packaging
TV/magazine advertisements
Delivery to shops
Wages for shop assistant and running store
Profit

**Costs of ready-made items include**
materials   labour   overheads (premises, equipment)   advertising   profits

Making a T-shirt

## Discuss

Using the example of the ready-to-wear T-shirt, discuss what you think is meant by these costs.
● materials  ● labour  ● overheads (premises, equipment)  ● advertising
Why do you think businesses want to make a profit?

Testing out your design is a way of finding out how good it is and whether your ideas work. When you think about testing, ask yourself questions like these.

- Does the design meet the **design brief?**
- Does it work?
- Is it safe to use?
- Is it attractive to look at?

You should be quite honest with yourself. Think of ways you could improve your design, even if you can't carry them out.

## Testing for real

1 A group of students designed an early reading game. They tested their design by taking the game to the local infants' school. Results? The children enjoyed playing with it and teachers said it helped with reading and maths!

The students' game

The nursery overall

2 A group of students designed this overall for nursery school children.
How could they set about testing their design?

**3** Davida Bates often mislaid her oven gloves. She designed these oven gloves which were attached to her apron! How could Davida's design be tested?

The wet suit

Davida Bates and her oven gloves

**4** This brightly coloured wet suit was designed for sailing and water sports. How could this design be tested?

## Discuss

In groups discuss ways you could test the following designs:
- a new biscuit recipe
- a garden designed for blind people
- an area designed for recycling paper, cans and clothing
- a tea party menu for a group of elderly people
- a container for holding cassettes or records

Now think of designs for yourselves which you could test out.

# Setting up tasting panels

When you invent new recipes or want to compare food products, you need to *taste* them to decide which you like best. Get other people to help and give their views by setting up a **tasting panel**.

How will you test and taste?

You have five senses to make you aware of the food you eat:

sight taste smell touch hearing
– *use them!*

SIGHT: COLOUR,SHAPE TEXTURE

HEARING: HOW DOES IT SOUND WHEN YOU EAT IT SNAP CRACKLE

SMELL: FRESH, STALE, YUMMY

TASTE: IT'S SOUR, SWEET

TOUCH: IT'S NICE, AND CRISP

The five senses

**Brainstorm** your group (see page 14) to get ideas for words you could use to describe foods and drinks.

You could use this technique when tasting the cereal bars which you may invent recipes for on page 86, or compare factory made cereal bars.

*Key words for tasting*
*taste* sugary sweet burnt
*texture* – how it feels in your mouth – soft chewy crunchy tough
*appearance* colour shape size texture

## Blind tastings

If you are tasting ready-made food it is better not to know the product name. At a hamburger tasting, for example, if you knew that one of the hamburgers came from McDonald's you might think that you would like it best. So, each item of food should be placed on a plate and numbered or labelled instead of giving it a name.

Or the taster can be blindfolded.

Blind tasting

This is known as *blind tasting*.

### Organizing a tasting

To taste food, each person needs
- a glass of water
- a teaspoon if the food is runny
- a tasting chart

### Method
1 Taste each sample of food.
2 Write down your findings on your chart.
3 Have a sip of water to clear away the taste.
4 Wash your teaspoon each time.

### Tasting chart
You could draw up a chart like the one below to record your results.

|  | *Food 1* | *Food 2* | *Food 3* | *Food 4* |
|---|---|---|---|---|
| *Taste* |  |  |  |  |
| *Texture* |  |  |  |  |
| *Appearance* |  |  |  |  |

# Tasting panels

After a tasting session you need to sort out your results. You can sort them into order with the food you like best at the top.

| Cereal bar tasting | |
|---|---|
| 1st choice | B |
| 2nd choice | C |
| 3rd choice | A |
| 4th choice | D |

How can you work out which cereal bar your group liked best?

| | Ali | Emma | Jaweed | Nina | Tex |
|---|---|---|---|---|---|
| 1st choice | B | D | C | C | A |
| 2nd choice | C | B | B | D | B |
| 3rd choice | A | A | A | A | C |
| 4th choice | D | C | D | B | D |

Now move the results to a **tally** chart to work out the **rank order**, so that you can find the most popular choice.

| Results chart | A | B | C | D |
|---|---|---|---|---|
| 1st choice | / | / | // | / |
| 2nd choice | | /// | / | / |
| 3rd choice | //// | | / | |
| 4th choice | | / | / | /// |

Which cereal bar has the most tally marks?

| 1st choice | // | = C |
|---|---|---|
| 2nd choice | /// | = B |
| 3rd choice | //// | = A |
| 4th choice | /// | = D |

This gives the rank order with C the favourite recipe.

## Discuss

Suggest other ways of working out the results of a tasting. What other things can you test by sorting them into rank order?

# The art of tasting tea

Did you know that it takes at least five years to train as a tea taster?
This is how tea tasters organize their tastings. Each cup of tea must be made the same way.

**Method**
One tea bag in 200 ml boiling water, brewed for *exactly* four minutes. Serve with one tablespoon of milk.

The tea taster holds the tea in the mouth so that it passes all round the mouth. After a slurp, the tea is spat out. The taster must remember the flavour and smell of the tea to compare it with others.
They have nearly 100 words to describe tea tastes – 'bright', 'full bodied', 'brisk' . . .
Feel and smell are important too. The tea taster looks at wet and dry leaves and makes a note of the colour and evenness of the leaves. How do they judge the best? Well, teas are so different, it depends upon what you like!

Tea tasters

## Evaluate

Hold your own tea tasting. Follow the method used by the tea tasters.
Compare brands of tea bags. Think of your own words to describe the taste, feel and smell.

When you have completed your design, you need to **evaluate** the *whole* of your work. This helps you think about how well things went and what improvements you could make in the future.

What do you think?

## Evaluation checklist

- Evaluate as you go along.
- Remember to keep a record of any changes or problems you face and how you solve them.
- Ask other people for their views.

**Your research**
- How did it go?
- How did your research affect your design proposal?

**Your plans**
- How did the planning go?
- Which parts of your planning did you find easy or difficult?
- What changes did you make to your plans and why?
- What were the **constraints** (limits) on your design?
- How did these constraints affect your design?

**Making your design**
- How did your plan affect your work?
- What things went well?
- What changes did you make and why?

- Did any skills need more practice and why?
- How well did you use your **equipment?**
- How successful were your methods?
- How safely did you work?

Skills and safety

## Final evaluation
- What was the aim of your design?
- How well does your design meet this aim?
- Are you pleased with the result? Why/why not?
- What do other people think?
- How could you improve your design?

A better design

# How does "Which?" evaluate things?

*Which?* magazine is used by people who want accurate and honest advice on things they buy or the services they use. How does the *Which?* team set about comparing and **evaluating** products? The illustrations on these pages show a group of pupils acting out the steps taken to produce the *Which?* report 'Oh for a glass of orange!'

## Oh for a glass of orange!

Genuine orange squash is at least a quarter real orange juice. But our tasters thought the squashes tasted no more like 'natural orange juice' than the rest

Testing orange drinks
*Source: Which?* July 1987

## Steps in evaluating a product

### 1 Discussion of ideas
The *Which?* team meet and come up with ideas.

*There are so many kinds of orange juice for sale.*

*Let's investigate them.*

Discussion

They decide upon their aims.

> *Aims*
> To taste and compare the contents of different orange drinks.

### 2 Research
They need to discover the range of orange drinks for sale, their cost and where they are sold, so **questionnaires** (see page 16) are sent to food makers and shops to find out this information.

The questionnaire

### 3 Testing
Drinks for testing are chosen, then a selection of the drinks is bought from shops which do not know that people from *Which?* are buying the goods.

Which ones?

The drinks are delivered to the *test laboratory*. A **tasting panel** is set up to taste the drinks. The panel does not know which drink is which, and awards marks for *taste*, *colour* and *sweetness*. This is called a *blind tasting* (see page 68).

Testing different drinks

### 4 Evaluation
A report is written about the tasting then checked to see if the aims set out at the beginning have been met. The report is rewritten if necessary.

The final report is sent to others in the team for their comments and to see if the research and tasting are accurate. Any necessary changes are made.

The report is prepared for printing and designers work on the layout. It can take nine months, from start to finish, to prepare such a report!

The report: meeting aims?

# Report results

The final report

### Tasting and costs
*Our panel of 75 keen squash and drink tasters (all 14 years and over) compared the products. The manufacturer's instruction for the brands was 'dilute to taste'.*

### Verdict
*Our tasters couldn't pick a favourite dilutable drink of any category. If you are concerned about whether they contain specific additives, check the ingredients list carefully. Otherwise just go for the taste, sweetness and price that suits you.*

## Test and evaluate

Evaluate a product for yourselves. You could use this *Which?* report to give you ideas and sort out a plan of action.

## Plan

**Brainstorm** your group to get ideas (see page 14).
What are the *aims* of your test?
Collect the products you want to test – you could start with orange drinks.
Set up a tasting or testing panel.
Write a report on your results.
Give your *verdict* – a product evaluation.

Kelda Free aged 13 years, who goes to school in Singapore, designed a useful wall tidy for her bedroom. As she planned her design she thought about the choices she could make with the layout, **materials** and the way she worked. As she progressed, she **evaluated** her work at different stages, before making her *final* evaluation.

1.  Kelda drew some designs then commented on
    - how well each design worked
    - what materials she could use
    - how pleasing she found each design.

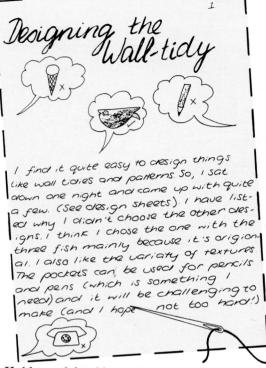

2.  Kelda explained how she chose her design and why it meets her needs.

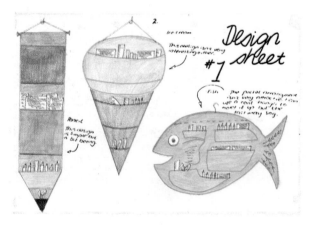

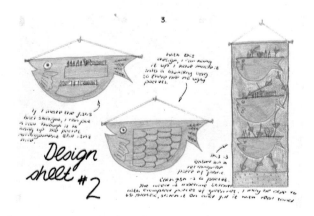

3.  Money matters! Kelda described how she chose the material.

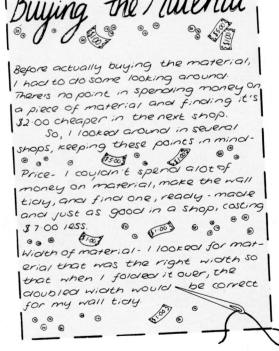

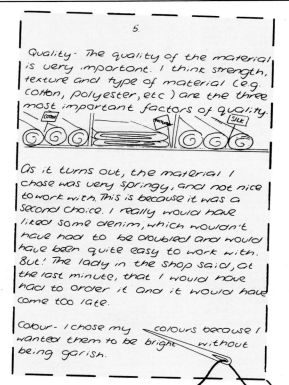

5.

**Quality** - The quality of the material is very important. I think strength, texture and type of material (e.g. cotton, polyester, etc.) are the three most important factors of quality.

As it turns out, the material I chose was very springy, and not nice to work with. This is because it was a second choice. I really would have liked some denim, which wouldn't have had to be doubled and would have been quite easy to work with. But! The lady in the shop said, at the last minute, that I would have had to order it and it would have come too late.

**Colour** - I chose my colours because I wanted them to be bright without being garish.

**4** Changes, changes – Kelda had to make a snap decision and change plans.

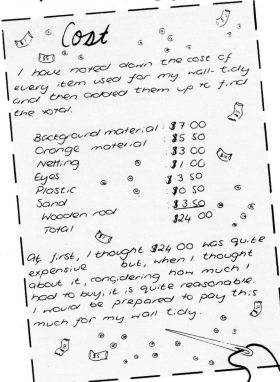

## Cost

I have noted down the cost of every item used for my wall-tidy and then added them up to find the total.

| | |
|---|---|
| Background material | $7.00 |
| Orange material | $5.50 |
| Netting | $3.00 |
| Eyes | $1.00 |
| Plastic | $3.50 |
| Sand | $0.50 |
| Wooden rod | $3.50 |
| Total | $24.00 |

At first, I thought $24.00 was quite expensive but, when I thought about it, considering how much I had to buy, it is quite reasonable. I would be prepared to pay this much for my wall tidy.

**5** Counting the cost – Kelda evaluated the final cost of the wall hanging.

## Evaluation

I had a lot of fun designing my wall-tidy and I think the design is both interesting and original. I like the different textures and colours I have used.

I took quite a while to complete my wall-tidy but I am very pleased with it.

Although it was a lot of work, the sewing was quite easy, except for the hand sewing on the "plastic pocket" and the final hem at the top of the background piece.

I am very happy with my finished product. It is a pity it can't be washed because of the sand.

Kelda Free 3JCC

**6** How well did it all go? – the *final* evaluation of the project.

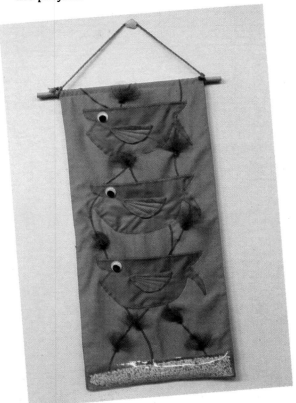

The wall hanging tidy

*Side by Side* is a scheme started in 1982 to help young and old people get to know each other better. Elderly people visit schools and work with pupils. They can provide much valuable information about past ways of life and how and why things have changed.

For the scheme to work successfully, each school carries out a regular **evaluation**, so that any problems can be sorted out as soon as they arise. They use three methods of evaluation.

## 1 Discussion
Young and old meet together and talk about how they feel about the project. This helps with ideas for the future and to see how things are going.

Let's find out what it was like being young years ago

Talking about the project

## 2 Questionnaires
Some people don't want to talk, so this simple **questionnaire** can be used (see page 16).

---

**Side by Side Questionnaire**

Name (optional)

Day(s) of attendance:

1 What activities have you particularly enjoyed?
2 What activities have you not enjoyed?
3 How could group activities be improved?
4 What have you personally gained from the experience?
5 What changes, if any, would you like to see introduced?
6 Any other comments.

---

## 3 Diary
Young and old can both complete a diary to describe their activities and feelings. This could be used for group discussion.

*Side by Side* says about the evaluation:
*Both young and old will show greater enthusiasm if they are drawn into the evaluation process.*

## Discuss

Why do you think the evaluation of this project is important? How does it help young and old people to work better together? What kind of project could be designed for your school in which young and old people could work together and exchange ideas?

*Side by Side*

### Designs which didn't work!

William Heath Robinson was an illustrator who was famous for his crazy drawings of unlikely inventions. What do you think about his drawings for designs to look after children?

First lessons in walking

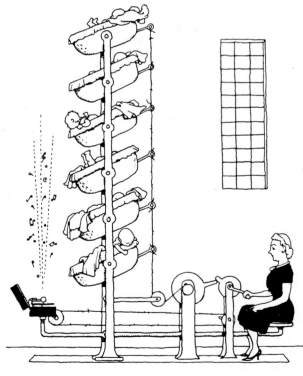

Six-tier communal cradle

Heath Robinson's designs

## Evaluate

Discuss and **evaluate** Heath Robinson's ideas. Would they work? How could the designs be improved? Record your findings. Draw up ideas of your own.

### A clock that makes the tea

The teasmade
*Source:* Trustees of the Science Museum

## Evaluate

Look closely at the advertisement for this teasmade of 1904.
Do you think this invention will sell well? What sort of person would find it useful? Give your reasons. Write an evaluation of this product.

# Designs in trouble

Sometimes carefully tested designs just don't work out in real life.

## The story of the Sinclair C5

In 1985, Sir Clive Sinclair invented a little battery-powered tricycle – the Sinclair C5. He wanted his design
- to be quiet and pollution free
- to run on electricity
- to be cheap to buy and to run.

His Sinclair C5 met his design aims.
- It could be recharged from the home electricity supply and run at 15 miles per hour for a 20 mile range.
- It cost only £399 including battery charger and safe driving book.

However, when it was launched one critic called it 'The most useless of vehicles, the washing machine powered C5 trolley'.

So what went wrong?
- Not many people bought the C5 – they said it was embarrassing to drive!
- There were worries about its safety.
- Some C5s broke down and had to be pedalled.

## Try again

A special team of teenagers was recruited to take the C5s around London to boost sales. But Sir Clive ran into money and factory production problems, and the price dropped to £139.99. The last 7000 models to be made were sold to the oil-rich sheiks in the Middle East!

## *Evaluate*

In busy towns and cities we are concerned about pollution and noise. What do you think was wrong with Sir Clive Sinclair's design and how could it be improved to sell again? Write an evaluation of the C5.

Sir Clive Sinclair and the C5

# Presenting your designs to others

A presentation needs to be carefully *organized*. You probably worked in a group. Think about the following points.

- How did you get along with others?
- Did the group work well?
- How did you share the tasks?
- How did you make decisions?

## Planning your presentation

Use the design and technology checklist (see page 92) to help you plan your presentation. You might find these headings useful when planning your work.

> Design ideas   Problems
> Research findings   Testing
> Constraints   Evaluation

## Presenting your ideas to others

If you worked in a group, then why not present as a group?
How will you present your design?

> display   talk   tape slide show
> video   cassette recording

## Planning a talk

- How long should your talk last? (Five to fifteen minutes is enough.)
- Will you share the talk between the group?
- Have you got some notes or a *script*? Give a script to each group member.
- Have you organized displays, photos, charts and plans?
- Have you had a practice, trial run of the talk?
- Are you prepared to answer questions?

Presenting ideas

## Who is your audience?

| a teacher    a group of students |
| parents or visitors    an expert |

- Do you need to give them handouts?
- Can everyone hear what you are saying and see well?

## Being a good audience

Listen carefully to others when they are presenting their work. Support and help them so that they do well. Ask sensible questions about what they did – for example, 'Did you have any problems?', 'Did you finish everything?'
Give them a clap when they have finished this difficult task!

The audience

## Special equipment

Some special **equipment** can be used to help with design and presenting. Videos, tape slides etc. can be used, and other equipment to help your design look neat.

### Photocopiers
How can a photocopier be used to help with your design?
- You can make several copies of pages for surveys or handouts.
- You can copy photographs.
- You can enlarge or reduce drawings and text.

**Check the cost of photocopying before you start!**

### Word processing using a computer
Try using a word-processing package on a computer.
- It helps you type out work neatly – this book was written with the help of a word-processor!
- You can change the text on the screen and sort out spelling mistakes.
- Some programs have different type styles and sizes (called fonts), so you can present your work in a more interesting way.

Special equipment: photocopier and fonts

# Displaying your work

All types of display – wall displays, books, folders . . . need to be carefully planned.
Will your display be 2D – flat like a wall display? Or is it 3D – three dimensional – with **models**, **prototypes**, the finished design?

*No-one's going to know how good your design is unless you present it well!*

Discussing the display

## Planning a 2D display

Plan out your display first. This will help you to organize the space. Keep your display clear and simple.

Think about what you want to show.
- your research
- photographs
- sketches
- working drawings

Work out the headings and the written text that you need.

### Lettering
Neat letters can be written using
- special pens
- lettering stencils
- desk top publishing programs
- cut out letters

### Mounting your work
Mounting a display improves the way it looks. Use coloured paper or card to give impact.

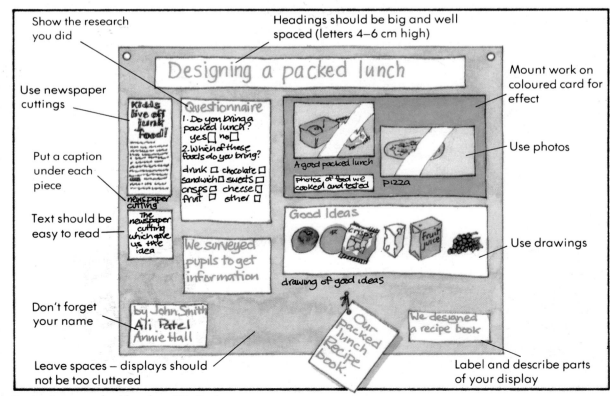

Show the research you did

Headings should be big and well spaced (letters 4–6 cm high)

Use newspaper cuttings

Put a caption under each piece

Text should be easy to read

Don't forget your name

Leave spaces – displays should not be too cluttered

Mount work on coloured card for effect

Use photos

Use drawings

Label and describe parts of your display

Designing a packed lunch: a 2D display

## 3D displays

If you are showing models, prototypes or things you have made, you may need to display them on tables or even boxes. For an attractive display, cover surfaces with paper or coloured material.

## A design folder

As you work, it is important to keep a record of what you have done. A design folder can help organize and show your work to its best.

Start with a *title page* with your name and a description of your design.

The *contents page* is important to show the order of work in the folder.
Number all pages and label them with headings.

You could organize your pages like the ones shown below.

Make sure all the work is neatly presented. Do untidy pages again and throw away messy work. Include your sketches, drawings and photos in the folder. You may also include sample materials and colour schemes.

Make a list of books and other **data** which you have used in your research.

## *Discuss*

How could you display some work which included
- a tape slide show
- a selection of food
- a musical jingle
- a computer designed game?

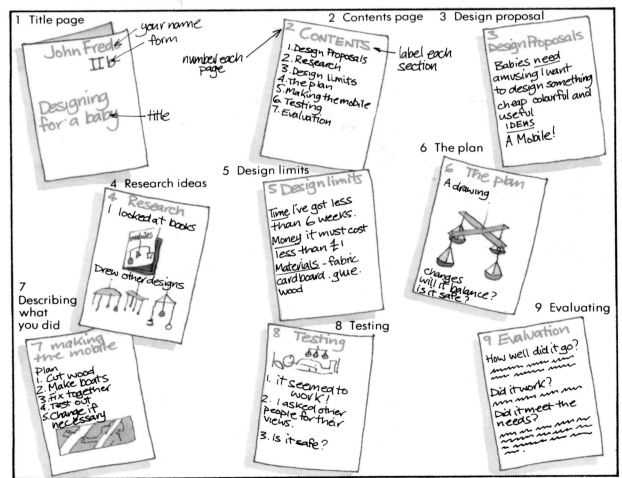

Pages and pages: presenting a design folder

# Making a tape slide show

A tape slide show is a way of putting together pictures from slides and tape recorded music, sounds or words.

Before you begin, think about your *aims* – what are you trying to show? Let's take an example.

There may be blind, partially sighted or disabled pupils in your school. People in wheelchairs could arrive for a visit. How easy is it for these people to get around?

## *Ideas*

Identifying problems

Things to photograph

**How can a tape slide show help with this project?**

As the group works, you could photograph (as slides) your findings, and keep notes of what you are doing.

## *Plan*

Photographs or stills are expensive, so make *plans* of what to record. You may decide to look at stairs, busy corridors at breaktime, queuing for school meals, going to the loo.

Choose about 10 things you want to photograph.

Improvements

In what ways could the area be improved?
- ramps for wheelchairs
- rails along the corridors for blind people
- better corridor organization
- safe queuing for food

## Putting the tape slide show together

Plan the show as a storyboard.

## STORYBOARD

**SLIDE 1**

Slide of wheelchair outside school unable to get in.

TEXT

The first problem a person in a wheelchair faces is how to get into our school.

**SLIDE 2**

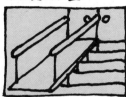

Slide of special ramp.

So we designed a special ramp.

**SLIDE 3**

Slide of us doing a survey.

We asked people in wheelchairs about how they got around.

Storyboard

1 Each slide needs a short piece of writing to explain what it is about.
2 Write a script to go with the slides.
3 Record the script on to a tape.
4 Test out the tape with slides to see if you need to make changes.
5 Think about your audience – is the show entertaining?

**Who will watch the tape slide show?**
Who will you invite to be the audience?
If you were showing how difficult it is for people in wheelchairs to get around your school, many people would be interested in seeing your findings.
● the school architect
● disabled people

### Evaluation

How can you **evaluate** the effect of a tape slide show?
One way is to ask the audience for their views!

### Discuss and record

Imagine that your group is going to present a tape slide show. You could choose a topic like 'Our school', 'Litter' — or think up your own ideas. Write down your *aim* — what you intend to show. Make a list of five photos you could take. Design a storyboard to present your show. Who will see the tape slide show and how will you evaluate its effectiveness?

# Cooking up an idea – designing a cereal bar

Look closely at *labels* to get ideas.

*Source:* Mars Confectionery

## Discuss

- What recipes can you use to make a cereal bar?
- What types of cereal bar are on sale?
- What snacks do teenagers like to buy?

## Getting ideas

## Research

How can you design a recipe?
What ingredients can you afford to use?
What ingredients do food makers use?
You could use *recipe books* and adapt ready tested recipes.

Comparing labels

---

### Nutty flapjacks

**Ingredients**

125 g margarine
125 ml clear honey
75 g brown sugar
250 g rolled oats
50 g chopped nuts

**Equipment**

saucepan, wooden spoon, tablespoon, greased baking tray (18 × 28 cm), knife, cooling rack

**Method**

1 Set the oven at 180°C/Gas 4.
2 Melt the margarine, honey and sugar in a pan. Stir in the oats and nuts and mix well.
3 Turn into a greased baking tray and smooth down.
4 Bake in the oven for 25–30 minutes. Cool in the tin for 2 minutes.
5 Cut into 20 slices and remove from tray.

What can you *afford* to make?

| | | |
|---|---|---|
| **40p** 250g | **55p** 100g | **70p** 500g |
| **80p** 125g | **60p** 1kg | **90p** 250g |
| **30p** 500g | **70p** 750g | **80p** 250g |

Costing it out

## Design and make

Record the findings from your research and come up with **design proposals** for cereal bars. Choose one to try out.

Plan how you will test out your ideas.

You could use a timeplan.

| Timeplan to make nutty flapjacks | |
|---|---|
| Time | Order of work |
| 9.30 | Collect equipment and ingredients |
| 9.40 | Set the oven at 180°c/Gas 4 Grease baking tray |
| 9.45 | |

A timeplan

Test out your recipe. Record any changes you made. Does your recipe *work*?

Oh! It's burnt!

Ooops!

If not, try again.
Organize a **tasting panel** to vote for the best recipe (see page 68).
Write out the *exact* recipe.
Record your work.

## Plan and make

How could you try to sell your cereal bars? You could conduct a **survey** to find out what other pupils think about your ideas. If possible, have a *trial run* to test out if you can sell your design.
You need to think about
● food safety   ● rules on selling food
● your costs
How well did they sell?

A success story

What changes should you make?

## Evaluate

As you work you will have recorded changes that you made and explained why you made them. This all forms part of your **evaluation**. Now think about how successful you were, and what you could improve.

# Designing a children's book

Your class wants to invite some children from the local playgroup to your school to entertain them for the day. You decide to design a book for use on the day.

## Research

How do you go about making your design – a children's book? What sort of book will meet the *needs* of these children? You could *visit* the playgroup (see page 34) and find out what books they like.

I like funny stories

You can feel this book

I like books which move

You could *visit* a library (see page 36) and look at other children's books to give you ideas.

This book is useful and colourful

You can feel this book

long and thin   square

I like the way this monkey swings

You could *question* an *expert*.

What books do young children choose?

Keep a record of your findings.

## Plan

We could make up a story or a poem

Let's teach them how to get dressed

...Or show them foods from around the world

- What are the **constraints** (limits) on your design – time, money . . .?
- What will the book be about?
- What **materials**, tools and **equipment** can you use? Look at the ideas for materials in the next column.
- How much will it cost?
- Who will make the book and how will they do it?
- How will you keep a record of your work, and test out its success?

## What materials can you use?

List the materials you need — you could stick in **samples**. How much do they cost?

- Find out the cost of the different papers, fabrics, glues etc.
- Make sure you don't *waste* materials — plan first.

Choosing and costing materials

# Design and make

Make a *plan of work*.
**Sketch** your designs in *page layouts*.
Describe how you will put the book together.
Divide the tasks between the group.
Make your book.
Record any changes you had to make to your first design plan.

# Evaluate

How can you **evaluate** the finished book? Why not ask the children? They will tell you what they think!

You could write about, or tape record or even video the children as they use the book (see page 48).
Make a report on your findings.
Did it meet the needs of the children?
How could you improve the design?

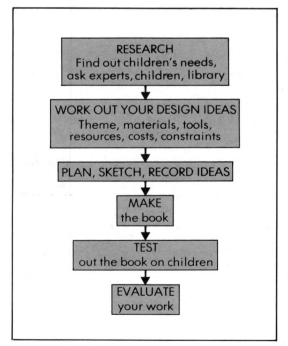

Stages in designing a children's book

The Schools Design Prize competition run by the Design Council gathers together design projects from secondary schools. Here is the work of three groups of pupils.

**Sarah Harbottle** started to get ideas for her game for young children by looking at different games and finding out the needs of children. She wrote a **design brief** then carried out more research to find out what children enjoy doing, the colours they like and their educational needs. She **sketched** out her ideas on paper then made up different games – cards, a top, a cube – and packed them in a colourful games box.

The games box

Ideas

### Research
Sarah started by asking questions and looking at existing designs. She also asked experts for advice.

**Pupils from Mill Hill County High School**, London, designed a Thermocoat for elderly people which would be warm, waterproof and lightweight. They had to find **materials** which would meet these needs, as well as being flameproof.

They wrote to companies for information and found out about safety standards. They collected samples of materials and did tests for insulation, water resistance and flammability. Since they wanted the coat to be seen in the dark, they looked at fluorescent materials. When Marks and Spencer plc. offered to supply material for the coat, they knew exactly what they wanted!

**Pupils from Sacred Heart High School**, Hammersmith, conducted a survey of 40 people to find out their favourite flavours for a new snack bar. They thought of several names and chose *Lottë Bar* from the word 'lots'. They designed eye-catching packaging with clear lettering which would be easy to produce on a large scale. They worked out the price of the snack bar by costing the ingredients, packaging, labour and profit.

Describing the design

*Materials*
Investigating and understanding materials is an important part of design. It helps to make decisions and come up with ideas. Choice of materials is affected by their safety, fitness for purpose, cost, how easily they can be used and **constraints** on manufacture.

The finished coat

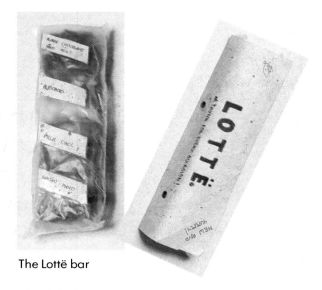

The Lottë bar

*Selling*
If a product is to be manufactured, the constraints of industry and the needs of the consumer have to be considered. With the Lottë Bar, pupils had to think about how it could be made on a large scale, and how to set about selling it.

# *Design and technology checklist*

## Identifying the needs or opportunities

The needs or opportunities .....................................................................................................
.........................................................................................................................................................

Ideas for design ........................................................................................................................
.........................................................................................................................................................

## Generating a design

Ideas from brainstorming .........................................................................................................
.........................................................................................................................................................
.........................................................................................................................................................

The idea I/we chose to design and make was ......................................................................
.........................................................................................................................................................

I/we chose this because ...........................................................................................................
.........................................................................................................................................................

The *aim* of the design is .........................................................................................................
.........................................................................................................................................................

The design will be    an artefact ☐    a system ☐    an environment ☐

*The constraints* on the design are ........................................................................................
.........................................................................................................................................................
.........................................................................................................................................................

In our research I/we used

| | | | |
|---|---|---|---|
| books ☐ | databases ☐ | questionnaires ☐ | telephone ☐ |
| newspapers ☐ | TV, radio ☐ | letters ☐ | photographs ☐ |
| magazines ☐ | video/films ☐ | interviews ☐ | visits ☐ |
| leaflets ☐ | diaries ☐ | Campus 2000 ☐ | case studies ☐ |
| experts ☐ | Teletext ☐ | observation ☐ | data ☐ |
| others ☐ | | | |

I/we recorded our results as

| | | | |
|---|---|---|---|
| notes ☐ | lists ☐ | photographs ☐ | drawings ☐ |
| bar charts ☐ | video ☐ | pie charts ☐ | others ☐ |

## Planning and making

I/we planned how we could make our design by

| | | |
|---|---|---|
| drawing a flow chart ☐ | keeping a diary ☐ |
| making a timeplan ☐ | making a list ☐ |

other ways .................................................................................................................................

I/we used

drawings ☐ diagrams ☐ models ☐ plans ☐

sketches ☐ storyboards ☐ others

The materials I/we decided to use were ..................................................................................

I/we chose these because ...............................................................................................

....................................................................................................................

I/we used this equipment.................................................................................................

....................................................................................................................

The new skills I/we learned were .......................................................................................

This is how I/we made the design ......................................................................................

....................................................................................................................

I/we tested our design by

testing/tasting panel ☐ asking others ☐ trying it out ☐

trial run ☐ other ..................................................................

I/we did/did not need to make changes in our design because ...........................................................

....................................................................................................................

I/we presented the work by ............................................................................................

....................................................................................................................

# Evaluating

The design does/does not meet the aim because ........................................................................

....................................................................................................................

These are the things that went well ...................................................................................

....................................................................................................................

These are the problems I/we had .......................................................................................

....................................................................................................................

I/we solved these problems by .........................................................................................

....................................................................................................................

These are the comments other people made about my/our design ..........................................................

....................................................................................................................

This is what I/we think about my/our design ...........................................................................

This is how my/our design could be improved ...........................................................................

....................................................................................................................

....................................................................................................................

**Analyse** Look at something carefully and criticize it.

**Artefact** An object made by people, such as a meal, leaflet, clothing, chair.

**Bar chart** A way of comparing results by drawing a series of bars on a graph.

**Brainstorming** A way of getting started by collecting everyone's ideas together.

**Constraints** Limits which affect design such as money, time and skills.

**Contexts** Situations where design and technology happens – for example, a meal can take place in the context of the home, school or community.

**Data** Facts and figures.

**Database** A collection of information or data stored on a computer.

**Design brief** Notes to explain the aim of the design.

**Design proposal** The idea for design, arising from a need or opportunity.

**Design specification** The exact details of the design ideas.

**Diagram** A drawing which shows how something works, using arrows or labels.

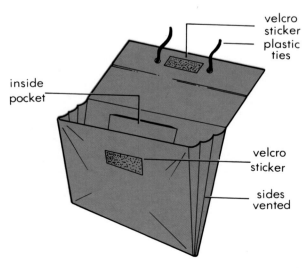

**Environment** Our surroundings – play areas, shops, rooms.

**Equipment** Tools and machinery.

**Evaluating** Judging how effective and successful you have been.

**Exploded view** A drawing with pieces of the object spaced out to explain how the design works.

**Facts** Things you can see, measure and check for yourself.

**Flow chart** A way of showing the stages of doing something.

**Logo** A symbol for a product or organization to identify them.

## British TELECOM

**Market research** The way businesses find out information before they launch a new product.

**Materials** What is used to make objects e.g. paper, glue, paint, food, clay, wood, fabric, plastic.

**Model** Something made in cheaper materials or smaller than real size in order to help you to understand your design ideas.

**Observing** Carefully watching something or someone and recording your findings.

**Opinions** People's views and feelings.

**Pie chart** Information presented in sections of a circle, like slices of a pie.

**Prototype** Accurate model of a design.

**Prioritizing tasks** Sorting tasks into order of importance.

**Questionnaire** A series of specially designed questions which form part of a survey.

**Rank order** A collection of items which have been tested and sorted into order, using several people's views.

**Resources**  The equipment, materials, skills and surroundings you have available to you to help with your design work.

**Role play**  Acting out the way other people behave in order to understand a situation better.

**Sample**  A group of people selected for a survey, which represents the views of many others; a typical example.

**Scale plan**  An exact plan of say, a cloakroom, drawn small enough to fit on the page or screen.

**Sketch**  A quick drawing using only a few lines to show design ideas.

**Skimming**  Glancing quickly through information to pick out important details.

**Spider diagram**  A quick way of presenting ideas from brainstorming.

We could design a club

Designing for fun

**Survey**  A way of finding things out by asking questions.

**System**  The way things work – a routine or method for doing something, e.g. queue or fire drill.

**Tally**  A way of recording results from a survey using dashes.

Tally

Number of people who own a bicycle

$\cancel{IIII}$ $\cancel{IIII}$ $III$ = 13

Tally marks

**Tasting panel**  A group who taste different foods and drinks and decides which they like best.

**Triggers**  Things to help spark off ideas, such as newspapers and posters.

# Index